SAVE OUR SLEEP

Helping your baby to sleep through the night from birth to two years

TIZZIE HALL

Vermilion
LONDON

Metric conversion table

The birth weight of babies can be measured in both imperial and metric measurements.

1 inch	2.54 centimetres		1 centimetre	0.394 inches
1 ounce	28.3 grams		1 gram	0.0353 ounces
1 pound	454 grams		1 kilogram	2.20 pounds

1 3 5 7 9 10 8 6 4 2

Published in 2010 by Vermilion, an imprint of Ebury Publishing
First published in Australia by Macmillan, an imprint of Pan Macmillan Australia, in 2006

Ebury Publishing is a Random House Group company

Copyright © Tizzie Hall 2006

Tizzie Hall has asserted her right to be identified as the author of this work in accordance with the
Copyright, Designs and Patents Act 1988.

The Random House Group Limited Reg. No. 954009

Addresses for companies within the Random House Group can be found at
www.rbooks.co.uk

A CIP catalogue record for this book is available from the British Library

The Random House Group Limited supports The Forest Stewardship Council (FSC), the leading
international forest certification organisation. All our titles that are printed on Greenpeace approved
FSC certified paper carry the FSC logo. Our paper procurement policy can be found at www.rbooks.
co.uk/environment

Printed in the UK by CPI Mackays, Chatham, ME5 8TD

ISBN 9780091929503

Copies are available at special rates for bulk orders. Contact the sales development team on
020 7840 8487 for more information.

To buy books by your favourite authors and register for offers, visit www.rbooks.co.uk

The information in this book has been compiled by way of general guidance in relation to the specific
subjects addressed, but is not a substitute and not to be relied on for medical, healthcare, pharmaceutical
or other professional advice on specific circumstances and in specific locations. Please consult your
GP before changing, stopping or starting any medical treatment. So far as the author is aware the
information given is correct and up to date as at January 2010. Practice, laws and regulations all
change, and the reader should obtain up to date professional advice on any such issues. The author and
publishers disclaim, as far as the law allows, any liability arising directly or indirectly from the use, or
misuse, of the information contained in this book.

This book is dedicated to the memory of my baby brother Richard,
whose own short life had such a big effect on the way I have lived mine.
To Richard: there will always be a special place in my heart for you.

CONTENTS

AUTHOR'S NOTE

From early childhood, all I ever wanted was a baby so that I could practise being a mummy. I was elated when at seven my baby brother Richard was born but, after just nine weeks, Richard died suddenly of cot death, also known as Sudden Infant Death Syndrome (SIDS). From this point I became the big sister to every baby I could find. When parents came to school to pick up their children I would dash to those with a baby and ask if I could have a cuddle. On Sundays I was not beside my family in their church pew but rather sitting in one with a baby I could hold. In retrospect, I think those parents allowed me to interact with their babies because they realised how deeply the loss of Richard had impacted upon me.

I was nine when it struck me that I could help parents understand the message in their baby's cry. I had regularly taken a neighbour's baby, Peter, out for a walk by myself, but one day his mother decided she would accompany us. After strolling for about five minutes, Peter started to cry and his mother immediately stopped to pick him up. When I counselled, 'Don't pick him up, that is his going-to-sleep cry,' she looked at me strangely. I explained that he always cried at this point during our walk but I never disturbed him because my mother had instructed me not to pick a baby up until I was on the green, where we played as children. By the time I got there, Peter would be fast asleep. That day his mother agreed to leave him until we'd reached the green, possibly to prove me wrong; however, baby Peter had fallen asleep just as I'd predicted.

It wasn't long before all the mums in our neighbourhood called me when they couldn't calm or comfort their crying babies. Very quickly I learnt to read their babies' body language and cries and I soon became known as the local baby interpreter. Over the years I have been labelled with all sorts of names, including the baby coach, baby whisperer, miracle worker and even the baby witch! Despite this last tag, I insist there is no magic wand or witchery involved!

After completing school in Ireland I moved to England to continue studying. While studying I worked as a part time nanny which enabled me to keep practising and refining my skills. My reputation as a baby whisperer spread, and it wasn't long before I was again receiving calls at all hours of the day and night from desperate parents seeking help with their babies. Always, and often within hours, I resolved problems such as babies not sleeping through the night, not taking their bottles, or refusing to give up their dummies. In 2002 I moved to Australia and soon discovered that the need for help was as great on this side of the globe.

Over the years, hundreds of parents have repeatedly told me the same two things: first, 'You should write a book,' and second, 'You should clone yourself so more parents can get help.' A book seemed the easier option.

This book is not a medical or scientific volume but a collection of tried and tested solutions and tips based on my many years of experience with babies and young children. Its main purpose is to help parents understand and avoid sleep problems in young babies and toddlers. Some parents might only discover it when they are already experiencing sleepless nights, but don't worry, it's never too late for help. You should extract the advice which best fits with your life and beliefs.

I am hoping this book will give parents the confidence to take control of their babies' behavioural patterns – and as a bonus give me more time to devote to my husband, Nathan, and our family!

Throughout, I have used real client case studies I have come across during my work to help explain problems you may encounter.

Although all names have been changed I am sure some clients will recognise themselves; so thank you for allowing me to use your case studies in this book.

I would like to say a big thank you to all the families who have shared their babies with me, to Kirstie Crosser for her time and energy in helping Save Our Sleep, to Alex Craig for publishing my first book and everyone at Ebury Publishing for all your help and support. This book would not have been possible without you all. To those parents who are new to Save Our Sleep, welcome. I hope this book will help you get even more joy and happiness from your new baby.

1

GETTING STARTED

Everyone needs sleep, whether you're a newborn of just a few weeks or a fully grown adult. While adults are pretty adept at putting themselves to bed and sleeping the night through, with children it can be a little more complicated. In this chapter I discuss the different factors that can affect how well your baby sleeps and how anything from routines through to how we react can make the difference between a night's uninterrupted sleep or the tossing and turning that comes with having an unsettled child.

Many people are not aware of how they sleep. We do not go to bed and sleep all night without waking; most adults surface at least twice during the night. During the night we sleep in cycles, drifting from light sleep to deep sleep. In between these stages we briefly come to the surface without awakening fully and may toss and turn, trying to get back into our original sleeping position, but usually we fall right back to sleep and have no memory of this in the morning. Understanding how we sleep will help you understand the way your baby sleeps.

SLEEP DEPRIVATION

Not getting enough sleep is a big problem for the body and mind; after all, sleep deprivation was used as a form of torture during the world wars. Unless you have looked after a baby that does not sleep, it is difficult to try to imagine what this is like.

Sleep deprivation can cause:
- depression
- short temper
- guilt
- mood swings
- fatigue
- irritability
- careless mistakes
- difficulty concentrating
- slower reaction times
- increased stress levels.

I am hoping this book will help parents avoid this slow form of torture!

Not all new parents will become sleep-deprived; you can manage with very little sleep for the first eight weeks or so. But when sleepless nights continue for months, sometimes even years, the results can be debilitating.

Mothers should try to get off to a good start. This means following the good old-fashioned rule of spending the first ten days after the birth mainly in bed, staying in your dressing gown and not tidying up or checking what has not been done in your absence! Try to take the phone off the hook at least once a day and attempt to have an uninterrupted nap for an hour or longer. Rushing around too much will make you more and more tired and may even cause your milk supply to suffer. Don't worry if around day four you start to cry: this is what they call the baby blues and it comes on as much from tiredness as from hormonal changes that are beyond your control.

While at first you may feel too tired to get all the normal daily tasks done, as the weeks go on these tasks can mount up. What was a couple of little jobs becomes hundreds of little jobs, all piled up into a great big mountain you can't seem to see past. The overall feeling I get from a lot of my female clients is an amazing sense of guilt. They feel guilty because the jobs aren't done or that there's no dinner for their partner when he returns from work. Sleep deprivation can mean they even feel too tired to go to their crying baby or change their baby's nappy and this makes them feel even more guilt. And then when sleep finally does come, your overactive mind might play games with you, waking you up in the middle of strange dreams which then prevent you from getting back to sleep.

This lack of sleep and energy causes many mothers to feel they are hopeless failures and that they are letting their partner down because he is unable to have a good night's sleep either and has to work during the day. Many of these partners tell me how they themselves feel guilty because they are not doing more to help. They feel bad for having to work each day, leaving their partner feeling alone and run-down, and explain how exhausted and worried they feel, and how this affects their own work.

With these pressures it's no surprise that the relationship between sleep-deprived parents can become strained. Couples who claim to have never fought before their baby was born tell me how they fight all the time over the silliest of things, like what to eat for dinner or who had the car keys last, and how they never make love any more because they are too tired.

After only a few days of sleep deprivation, the body undergoes changes similar to 'fast-forward' ageing: memory loss, metabolism problems and poor athletic performance. If sleep deprivation continues over the long-term, it increases the risk of more serious problems.

LET SLEEPING BABIES LIE (BUT NOT TOO LONG)

In the first few days, newborns can sleep from sixteen to twenty hours a day. The gender of the baby or whether she is breast- or bottle-fed makes no difference. It is very important in the early days to feed your baby frequently. As some newborns don't have the energy to wake and ask for food, I recommend that breastfed babies should go no longer than three hours in the day and five hours at night without a feed. This benefits your breastmilk supply as much as the baby's needs. Formula-fed babies can be given their bottle every four hours during the day and may be left for six hours between night feeds.

By week two it is important to be developing some sort of sleeping and feeding routine. For years health professionals have been debating the pros and cons of a routine, but the one factor they always agree on is that young children and babies feel safe and secure when they know what is going to happen and when.

The reason I recommend establishing a routine by two weeks old is to be sure your baby is sleeping correctly before she starts to sleep in daytime sleep cycles. Otherwise, problems such as catnapping may occur. The two most important rules when it comes to babies and sleep are:

- always put your baby down for a sleep or nap in the place you intend her to wake up; and
- try to teach your baby the skill of self-settling from as young as possible. This means going to sleep without aids, such as rocking, patting, feeding or even the use of a dummy.

THE IMPORTANCE OF A ROUTINE

I believe routines are very important and a big help to parents learning to interpret their baby's different cries. When following a routine, you will begin to distinguish between your baby's hungry, tired or bored cries because when she starts to cry, you will be able to look at the routine and see what is due next. If she is due a feed, you will start to recognise that as the hungry cry. If your baby is due to have a sleep, you will learn that is the tired cry. They do, in fact, sound different.

At first the idea of a routine can be quite scary. If I have to spend the day clock-watching, how will I relax or get on with everyday jobs? What happens if I have an older child, with a school run to do each day? Don't worry, it is possible. Not everyone's baby or life is the same, so sometimes routines need careful adjusting to suit your circumstances. If you find this to be your case, then try following my basic rules and adjust the routines to suit you better.

The feedback I get from parents is that routines make their lives easier. For example, organising things such as doctor's appointments becomes easier because you know what your baby will be doing at each stage of the day. If you have older children they will also gain advantages from your baby having a routine, as you will be better able to plan activities with them. The best part of these routines is that you know you will have time for yourself and your partner in the evening. The general feeling I get from parents who are not following a daily routine is that evenings are often their hardest part of the day.

My routines also help babies to feel safe and secure. Your baby will know that her needs are being met and she has no need to cry, resulting in a happy, contented baby.

When to start a routine

In my experience, babies don't start to surface between sleep cycles (the process of drifting between light and deep sleep) until they reach 6 kg (13.2 lb), usually around eight to sixteen weeks. This means you can help a newborn baby go to sleep and she will stay asleep for a long period; however, when an older baby starts waking between sleep cycles she may instead catnap during the day. Then at about 8 kg (17.6 lb), around five to seven months, she will also start to wake between night-time sleep cycles. This is why I recommend starting to establish a routine so early, teaching your baby to go back to sleep between cycles prevents sleep problems occurring.

You will notice I have slightly different routines for babies who are bottle-fed and those who are breastfed until eight weeks. This is because breastfeeding routines before eight weeks are based on the mother's needs, not the baby's needs, as a breastfeeding mother needs to feed more often in the first eight weeks to build up a good supply of breastmilk.

THE GOLDEN RULE OF THE SEVEN O'CLOCK BUS

Parents often explain to me that they have children who sleep solidly all night but are awake and demanding attention at the crack of dawn each day. So how do you get the perfect morning where your baby sleeps right through to 7 am?

Putting your baby or child to bed at 7 pm is the key to success. If you put your baby to bed any earlier or later, invariably you will cause your baby or child to wake up before she has had enough sleep. This is where once again we find ourselves talking about sleep cycles.

For example, Lily is eight months old. I put her to bed at 6.55 pm and by 7 pm she is sound asleep. Lily sleeps in 40-minute sleep cycles, so Lily sleeps a short cycle until 7.40 pm then with little fuss drifts into a long cycle of 80 minutes. But at 9 pm after this long cycle, she stretches, yawns, opens her eyes and has a look around. Nothing much has changed so she chooses to go into another sleep cycle, which is another short 40-minute one, followed once again by the longer 80-minute period. This takes us to 11 pm when she again wakes briefly and goes into another cycle. This continues throughout the night with Lily waking every two hours at 1 am, 3 am, 5 am and finally at 7 am, a perfectly good time to start the day.

But if we put Lily to bed about half an hour later at 7.35 pm to be asleep by 7.40 pm, look what happens. She sleeps again in 40-minute and 80-minute short and long cycles until it is finally 5.40 am. However, at 5.40 am it may be light outside, the birds are singing and Lily decides to make the most of this new day. Instinctively, she starts crying out to mummy or daddy to come and get her. Despite the fact that Lily has not had enough sleep, she has managed to wake herself up to the extent that it is impossible to get her back to sleep.

This is precisely why it's so important not to miss the seven o'clock bus!

HOW WE REACT

Quite often when parents are woken at 5 am, they make the mistake of treating the situation differently than if the disturbance took place at 1 am, thinking their baby has had too much sleep by 5 am to attempt resettling so their only option is to get both themselves and the baby up. Unfortunately, this not only teaches baby to keep waking at 5 am but it also means that she will have difficulty resettling if she wakes at 3 am one morning. Your baby will get very upset and confused at the different treatment as she will not understand the difference between 3 am and 5 am.

I believe that babies, toddlers and children who wake at 5 am and are not resettled are getting insufficient sleep. You end up with a very overtired and hyperactive baby and the only way out is to ask her to resettle, irrespective of how long it takes. Parents are often unsure about this suggestion, thinking that it will take several hours – it may well do so initially, but you have to be strong and stick it out longer than your baby will. If the solution was as simple as going to bed earlier, getting up with your baby at 5 am and starting the day earlier than usual, then I would advise that. But the problem is usually more complex as there always tends to be knock-on effects. For instance the baby could become confused by the mixed messages and start to test the boundaries in place for other sleeps throughout the day. This could also affect the way she changes sleep cycles during the night.

Early rising is a common problem and teaching your baby to resettle at 5 am is probably more important than sticking to the routine for the rest of the day. In fact if you don't resettle her you may as well throw out the routine for the rest of the day because you have changed it before you even started!

Toby's story

Toby's parents started using my approach on Toby when he was fourteen months old. After waking at 5 am and having maybe one hour's sleep during the day, Toby had been falling asleep on the breast at about 9 pm each night. As he had also been waking every hour or so from 11 pm until 5 am, it was not a pretty picture for Toby's mum and dad. Alison (Toby's mum) was getting up about seven times per night and seemed to be only able to coax him back to sleep with the help of feeding.

Frustrated, tired and beginning to resent Toby, Alison tried my tips on the suggestion of her doctor. After just two nights of following my routine and settling advice, Toby began sleeping uninterrupted from 7.20 pm until 5 am. This was complemented by a further two hours sleep during the day. Everything was looking rosy and Alison was elated that she had reverted to a 'normal' existence as a new mother.

However, about two months later things started to go downhill again and Alison contacted me. When I consulted with her in more detail I discovered that she had been so happy with the improvements that when Toby woke at 5 am she would bring him into her bed where they would both fall back asleep, sometimes for a further hour or more. Then one morning Toby woke at 3 am instead of 5 am and, without looking at the clock, Alison reacted as usual and brought him to her bed.

From then on Toby started to wake earlier and earlier until he was crying out for attention at 1 am and would not go back to sleep. Unfortunately, this meant that we had to start all over again, but this time Toby would have to learn to resettle himself at 5 am rather than being picked up and taken to bed with mum.

On the first night under this new plan, Toby woke at 1 am and Alison left him to resettle. It took Toby twenty minutes to get back to sleep and he then woke again at 3 am and went back to sleep in three minutes. However, when he woke at 5 am he took until 7.50 am to fall back to sleep. I had told Alison to wake him ten minutes after he fell asleep so she did. On the second night, Toby slept right through until 5 am and he then yelled until 6 am before sleeping until 6.50 am. On the third night, Alison woke at 7.10 am and jumped out of bed, terrified something was wrong with Toby, but she was thrilled to find that he was still sound asleep. Having learned how to resettle himself when waking up, Toby has had little trouble resettling since then.

Catching the seven o'clock bus has been one of the main factors I have found to help your baby sleep soundly until 7 am. However, if you are putting her to bed at 7 pm and she is still rising early then I suggest you refer to the section on Early Rising on page 180 for other reasons why babies might be rising early.

WHERE SHOULD BABY SLEEP?

When clients contact me with concerns about where everyone in the family should sleep when the new baby arrives, each case has to be looked at individually as every family and home environment is unique. The solutions to sleeping arrangements are many and should be flexible.

There are always different opinions as to where a new baby should sleep, but I feel your baby should sleep in the place that enables you to get the most rest. If you would sleep better with her in your room, then put her in your room. If every noise wakes you up and you feel you would get more sleep with her in a separate room, put her in her own room. But wherever she sleeps at first, I do recommend moving her by five months to where you would like her to sleep for most of her babyhood. The reason for this is that most babies do not develop night-time sleep cycles until after five months. If your baby is sleeping in your bed or bedroom when she learns to drift from one sleep cycle to the next, it will be a harder transition for her to move bedrooms and relearn this skill in a new environment. So if you are going to move your baby, do it before five months.

When a family already has one or more children and a new baby on the way, I always recommend that all necessary moves be made well before the new addition to the family arrives. There are two reasons for this. First, moving any children into a different room or the same room as a sibling for the first time is most likely going to produce a few nights of unsettled behaviour. This may very well manifest in late nights, resulting in early mornings, which is the last thing you need when you are already stretched physically and emotionally with a new baby. Second, you don't want your older children thinking that the new baby is pushing them out of their room.

> **Tip:** It is not safe to put a sheepskin under your baby's bedding as this adds to the risk of cot death.

Baby's room

I have never found the way a room is set up to cause any sleep problems; however, there are things that you should be aware of. Your little baby will grow up very quickly into an adventurous toddler, so keep this in mind when setting her room up. Avoid placing the cot close to curtain or blind cords and keep the cot well away from things you don't want your toddler to reach, such as shelves, light switches or the contents of changing tables.

Moses basket/bassinet or cot

There are all sorts of baby bed options out there these days, but I initially prefer moses baskets, also known as bassinets. When the time comes you can put the whole basket inside the cot for a few days and nights until your baby is used to the new bed. Swinging cribs are nice to look at but also tempting for people to rock them, and this rocking could very quickly become a sleep aid. I am not so keen on things such as a hammock because at some point you will have to put your baby through the transition from hammock to a big cot.

There is also no reason not to put your baby straight into a cot. If she is swaddled as I recommend, she will be quite happy to sleep in a big cot, and if you choose not to swaddle then the cot is also a better option because she won't wake herself by touching the sides as she might in the moses basket. Please be aware that I recommend you swaddle your baby from birth until they are showing signs of being able to roll while swaddled. For further information on why I recommend swaddling please see pages 64–66.

Whichever you choose, you will need at least three fitted cotton sheets (you will be surprised at how often they need to be changed). You will also need a few changes of pram sheets for your pram and at least twelve muslin squares for mopping up when your baby brings up milk.

When purchasing a cot, there are a couple of things I recommend you look closely at. Look very carefully at the height between the top of the mattress and the top of the guardrail. Your baby will be a toddler before you know it and you may regret your choice when she starts to climb out! Cots are adjustable so you will need to ask the shop to put them at the lowest setting and compare a few – there can be quite a difference between brands. I also only recommend cots that are slatted all the way around so as to maintain maximum airflow. I do not recommend cots that have solid ends, as new research is showing restricted airflow might be a factor in the number of cot deaths.

Blackout blinds

I have never found a need to darken a room so much that a baby can't see a thing. I know some experts believe it is the biggest cause of early rising, but if babies couldn't sleep in the light, why would they sleep when out and about in the car or pram? But if you have tried all my suggestions without success, blackout blinds could be worth a try.

Night-lights

I do not believe you should put a night-light in your baby's bedroom. Babies are born without fears and always putting a night-light on in their room could teach them that there is something wrong with the dark.

Additionally, the brain's pineal gland naturally produces a substance called melatonin when in a dark place, so if your baby has a night-light on it can interfere with this hormone being made. Melatonin is actually a natural sedative that automatically slows the body down in preparation for sleep and it follows that a baby sleeping in a dark room will produce more of this and therefore sleep better.

Mobiles and music

I have never found the need to remove mobiles or other toys out of a baby's sight at sleep time. A mobile over your baby's cot is perfectly all right until she reaches an age where she can stand up and grab it, when it should be removed.

Music is very good for a baby, but it should not be turned on at sleep times. If your baby falls asleep listening to music from a mobile or a CD player, it could become an aid which she will become dependent on every time she goes to sleep and every time she moves from one sleep cycle to the next. Having this music will not always be possible – for example, if you stay with friends or relatives or go on an aeroplane – and could make your life very difficult.

Tip: When tucking your baby in at night, you can use the light on your mobile phone as a torch.

Room temperature

For the first couple of days after you bring your baby home from hospital, you might like your house to be warmer than usual, but not quite as warm as in the hospital. If your home is centrally heated, the temperature I recommend is 20°C. It will not harm your baby to have the house cooler or warmer, but if you're trying to breastfeed, change nappies and bath your baby, this is a comfortable temperature. Once your baby is accustomed to her new environment you can adjust the temperature of your home slowly back to what the family is comfortable with.

However, I do recommend that you always keep your baby's nursery at 20°C. Some health professionals recommend having the baby's nursery between 16°C and 20°C but I have found anything below 20°C is too cool for a baby to sleep well and it can cause catnapping and night waking. (For more information please see page 183.)

Overheating or letting your baby get cold can play a part in increasing the risk of cot death. This is why it is very important to get her bedding correct. For the most up-to-date bedding guide please visit my website.

During the day, I always dress babies in layers and put one extra layer on than I am wearing. This is usually the best guide. If you go somewhere and feel hot, take a layer off your baby, and if you are feeling a bit chilly then put an extra layer on. Once she starts to crawl and then walk your baby/toddler may be warmer than you. At this stage you are better to adjust the layers according to your baby's individual needs.

Yes, you should avoid over- or underheating your baby, but she will only come to harm if you get it seriously wrong and she is freezing cold or so hot she is sweating. When checking your baby's body temperature, don't judge it by her hands and feet as it is normal for these to feel cooler than the rest of her body. You could check her temperature by feeling the back of her neck or her tummy. If you want to warm your baby's hands or feet up, use some mittens and socks instead of piling extra blankets on.

Many babies I go to see are too cold at night. All I need to do is put a warmer sleeping bag on, add a few layers of cotton or bamboo bedding and make the room a bit warmer and the baby sleeps all night. A lot of babies wake at about 4 am from being too cold. This is the coldest time of the night. Even if you go in at this point to put extra bedding on, it is often too late as your baby is so awake it is hard for her to go back to sleep. The best and most economical way to heat a baby's room is with an electric oil-filled column heater with its own thermostatic control. Remember, your baby will be colder than you at night, partly because she is so small and partly because she does not move around at night so she is not generating heat like an adult does. A good habit to get into is putting an extra cotton blanket on at night after the 'dreamfeed' (the feed given to your sleeping baby as part of my routines) or just before you go to bed. From eight weeks babies often have more trouble regulating their temperature, so a safe baby sleeping bag is an essential investment, along with cotton or bamboo bedding and blankets, to ensure your baby is warm enough to settle and sleep well. As babies get older a safe sleeping bag will also keep the baby on her back, in the safe sleeping position recommended by the Foundation for the Study of Infant Deaths (FSID), and delay your baby kicking her bedding off. For tips on what to avoid when purchasing a sleeping bag please see page 262.

Tips:

- If your baby wakes and moans, has a sweaty back or sweaty, wet clothes, it is a sign that she may be overheating.
- If your baby moves all around the cot, never lies still, often rolls onto her tummy, catnaps during the day, or wakes from 4 am or 5 am, it is a sign that she may be too cold in bed.

Clothing & swaddles

Bodysuits, bundlers and babygros

These are really the only clothes you need in the first few weeks. You will need at least twelve of each; try to buy them in packs of two or three to keep the cost down and look for 100 per cent cotton. I prefer bodysuits that do up under your baby's bottom to help protect her kidneys from the cold. On very hot days and warm nights you may dress your baby in just a bodysuit and nappy.

Babygros and bundlers make dressing a baby much simpler. Ensure that all outfits have a wide head opening and buttons at the crotch to make changing easier. Two-piece outfits may look cute but the top can ride up and become uncomfortable. I have also noticed babies get quite uncomfortable in outfits with a waist. I have found that babies sleep better in sleepsuits and babygros than in two-pieces. I recommend a baby is not put in a two-piece outfit for any sleep before 18 months of age. Don't purchase any sleepwear with a hood as it can increase the risk of cot death and a hood can be quite bulky and awkward when lying down. Outfits with feet in them are practical as you will not need booties or socks that may fall off. And a warning that suits with buttons on the back instead of the front will drive your baby crazy: babies don't usually like to be laid on their tummies while you do them up.

Cardigans, jackets and snowsuits

If you have your baby in winter you will need two or three cardigans, preferably made of wool or cotton. Winter babies will need a snowsuit (try to find one that is machine washable). All babies will need a lightweight jacket, even summer ones. These jackets are good on warm but not hot days for outdoors, but also good on a colder day if you are going out and popping your baby in the car. If your baby is in the car in a heavier jacket she might overheat.

Socks and booties

For outfits that do not have feet, socks or booties will keep baby's feet warm in winter and protect them from the sun in summer.

Hat or bonnet

When going out and about, one broad-brimmed cotton hat in summer or a soft, warm hat that covers the ears in winter will be just the thing. As mentioned, never allow your baby to sleep in a hat or bonnet as she may become overheated, increasing the risk of cot death.

Bundlers

Bundlers are similar to babygros but open at the bottom, useful when changing nappies at night. However, a soft babygro outfit will do just as nicely when baby is a newborn and will save on additional clothing and expense.

Wraps/Swaddles

Most newborn babies love to be swaddled. Muslin swaddles are ideal for this because they give the baby security but still allow free movement of air and are especially good for summer. You will need at least three swaddles in either a stretch cotton or bamboo fabric because these breathe and the stretch helps keep the baby secure. Alternatively, the best swaddle I have found on the market and recommend for swaddling right up until your baby is showing signs of rolling while swaddled is the Doublewrap.

SIBLINGS

If you are admitted to hospital to delay premature labour, you should be careful how you approach this with your older children. You should always be as honest as possible; give a brief explanation and give true answers to any questions asked. If you don't have the answers, then tell them you don't know and are happy to ask the doctor for them.

Don't tell older children that their Mummy will be home after she has had the baby because quite often a mother is allowed home when the risk of the baby being too premature is over. It can be very hard to explain to a young child that the baby has not come yet, and then when you do go in to have the baby, your older child may be frightened you will be gone for the same amount of time.

In this type of situation and when you go in for the birth, it is not always best for your older children to visit their Mummy in hospital every night. If every time you bring a toddler in to see Mummy, it ends in tears and tantrums when you try to leave, it might be better for your toddler not to go through that each night. If your child can talk, then wait until they ask to see Mummy or ask them if they would like to.

When bringing a new baby home from the hospital, it is wise to have someone else with you to look after the new arrival. Even as you go into the house, it is best to have your hands free to kiss and cuddle your older children. It is always better if you can limit your attention to the new baby on the first day and try to give lots of attention to an older toddler or children. Most people say you should split your time between your new baby and older children, but I feel this is a bit unfair on the first day, as the new baby has had all your attention while you were in hospital.

Be very careful that all your visitors know not to run past the existing children to see the new baby. It is also a good idea for the new baby to give any older children a present when they first meet. If people such as grandparents are giving the baby a present, you could ask them to give your older children something small as well.

BABYTALK

I believe you should talk to she as if she is an adult from day one. Start by telling her what you are going to do to her rather than just doing it, for example, before pulling her legs up to change her nappy, explain why. This helps your baby to feel much more in control and will give her a feeling of security.

The latest research also shows that talking to your baby builds neural circuitry in the brain, which can help her learn language more quickly. Within the first few weeks she is already listening to you and within the first three months she is 'talking' to you. You will not understand what she is trying to convey but those gurgling sounds are conversations your baby is having with you. If you say something to your baby and wait for a response, she will make babbling sounds back. Try not to talk over your baby – stop talking and listen to what she is trying to say.

As your baby gets older, ask for her cooperation when doing things such as bathing or changing a nappy. 'Can you lift your bottom?' Even if you know she can't lift her bottom, it is still nice to let her feel involved and this will help her to learn more language.

Tell your baby when you are leaving the room and when you will be back. A protest may follow, but she will eventually understand the fact that you will return shortly.

Other ways of talking with your baby are to copy their noises and hold a 'conversation' by taking turns at making the noises. And it's never too early to read books to her, describing the pictures, colours, shapes, numbers and letters. Sing songs and nursery rhymes, play peek-a-boo, clap hands, make funny faces and sit in front of a mirror with your baby. As she gets older, try putting a sticker on her face then sitting her in front of a mirror – if she reaches for the sticker in the mirror she is not aware it is her reflection, but if she takes the sticker off herself she is.

COMMON QUESTIONS

Why are some babies born yellow? Newborn babies are often born with a touch of jaundice, caused by a high level of the chemical bilirubin in their blood. Your baby's liver should break it down within a couple of weeks.

How much weight will my baby lose after birth? Newborns can lose up to 10 per cent of their birth weight by the time they are ten days old.

Why is my newborn baby's bellybutton sticky? Before the end of the umbilical cord falls off (after about two weeks), it may seem a little sticky and leave a little smear of blood on the cotton wool you clean around it with, but this is nothing to worry about. Turn over the top of the nappy to keep the cord exposed to the air and help it dry. If it's weepy or surrounded by red skin, tell your midwife or baby health clinic nurse.

How do I tell if my baby is too hot or cold? As most babies have cold hands and feet because of their immature circulation, check by feeling the back of your baby's neck or her tummy under her clothes. Use thin layers of clothes so you can adjust baby's temperature easily. As a rough guide, babies need one more layer of clothes than you do.

Why does my baby look cross-eyed? Newborn babies often look cross-eyed when they're learning to focus. As their eye muscles get stronger this should disappear, though if you still notice this at six months or there is a family history of this, talk to your GP.

When can I take my new baby out of the house? Well, unless you had a homebirth, she's probably already made the journey home from the hospital so she's had her first taste of the outdoors. It's fine to take your new baby for a short walk or over to a friend's house. Just make sure you dress her appropriately, putting her in one more layer than you need yourself to feel comfortable.

Is it normal for my hair to be falling out in clumps? Yes, this is normal. During pregnancy you don't lose as much hair as usual, so your hair feels much thicker. After the birth of your baby, when your hormones settle down, your hair loss goes back to normal. Sometimes you lose all the hair you would have lost if you had not been pregnant. Don't worry, you will only lose what you would have in the forty weeks of pregnancy.

Should I use blankets as well as putting my baby in a sleeping bag? I have always thought of a sleeping bag as an extra layer of clothes which keeps your baby warm and delays a baby rolling to her tummy and kicking her blankets off. So a sleeping bag should be used with cotton or bamboo blankets and the amount of blankets should be adjusted depending on where you live and how warm and humid the nursery is.

2

FEEDING IN THE FIRST TWO WEEKS

Debate still rages over the benefits of demand versus routine feeding but the fact remains that babies thrive on routine and the security of knowing that their needs are being met in a consistent way. In my experience, babies who are given a defined daily routine are more content. They tend to adapt to life more easily than those who are conditioned to making demands and then expect their parents to meet those demands every time.

ROUTINE FEEDING IN THE FIRST TWO WEEKS

For years I have been studying different babies and breastfeeding mothers trying to work out why babies on a routine sleep better than those who are not. One aspect I considered is whether the quality of the mother's milk changes when she puts her baby on a routine. Because cow's milk is close to human milk, which is why we drink it and feed it to our children – I decided to discuss it with various dairy farmers.

Dairy farmers stick to strict routines in relation to their milking. Most will milk their cows at 5 am and 3 pm every day. When I enquired why, it was explained to me that milking the cows at a set time every day meant their metabolism knew exactly when and how much milk to produce.

The farmers said that if they milked their cows earlier or later than scheduled, the milk would not be of the highest quality or quantity.

It's not such a leap to come to the conclusion that this might be the same for a breastfeeding mother's milk supply.

Often when a mother seeks help about her unsatisfied, non-sleeping baby, the conclusion is drawn that the baby is hungry and the introduction of solids or formula is recommended, leaving the mother feeling that her breastmilk is inadequate. When she puts her baby onto formula, before long she has a contented baby, reinforcing the perception that her breastmilk was the problem. But what I have observed here is that with the formula comes a feeding routine for the baby. So was her milk not satisfying her baby in the first place or was her baby needing a routine? If she had decided to try a routine before giving up on her breastfeeding, would she have also had a contented baby? My experience leads me to believe that she would.

Another thing to take into account here is if your baby knows you will keep offering him a snack every couple of hours, he will never feel the need to have a full feed. Putting your baby on a routine gets him into the habit of filling right up when you offer the breast or bottle, because he soon learns it will be quite some time before you make the offer again. You will find he will feed for longer when on a routine, resulting in a fuller tummy which will help him to sleep better.

Also, be conscious that some babies think your sole purpose in life is to help him fall asleep. If your baby is tired and used to falling asleep every time you feed him, he may refuse to feed if he doesn't want to sleep. This is a problem I have frequently observed in babies not on a routine.

Again, the choice is yours. If you are finding demand feeding easy and you have no problem interpreting your baby's cries, you are doing well and should continue with what is working for you. However, if you are concerned that your baby is not eating and sleeping well because all he does is cry, then I recommend you try putting him on a set feed and sleep routine (explained later), especially before you give up on breastfeeding.

DEMAND FEEDING IN THE FIRST TWO WEEKS
The advice given to most new parents these days is to feed their baby on demand. This works really well for some mothers and babies but it's important to understand what demand feeding means: not

feeding your baby whenever he cries but feeding whenever he cries a *hungry* cry.

Following my routines will mean your baby seldom has a reason to cry, but when he does you should try to listen to the cry and interpret what he is saying. The good thing about my routines is that when your baby starts to cry, you can look at the routine and see what is due to happen next, a real help when learning to distinguish tired and hungry cries.

The most important cry to recognise is the emotional cry, as this is when you need to comfort your baby and try to find out the cause. One of the most common causes of this cry in a baby under two months is hunger. The cry of an emotional or hungry baby is continuous with no pauses and doesn't change pitch or tone, something like 'waa, waa, waa, waa, waa'. This cry I would never ignore and the first thing I would try is a feed.

A protesting cry, on the other hand, I feel is perfectly all right to ignore. The most common time you will hear this is when your baby is fighting sleep, and there will be gaps in the crying and the tone and pitch will go up and down. You should hear the pauses getting longer as he starts to fall asleep. If you are watching your baby, you will see him shut his eyes and nod off, then he will jump as though realising he is falling asleep and yell again.

Most parents will learn to interpret the different cries of their baby, but for new parents in the first two weeks this is nearly impossible. To the new mother, every cry sounds as though the baby is being tortured and this can cause a few problems if the one and only solution is to give him a feed.

Demand feeding – good or bad?

In order to establish breastfeeding, your new baby should be put to the breast frequently in the early days to stimulate the milk supply, but one possible problem in asking babies to demand their feeds is that some just don't have the energy to wake up and do so. Other babies are very 'sucky' and if given the chance will stay on the breast sucking all day and night. This mother could end up with very sore and even cracked and bleeding nipples, especially if she is too exhausted to correctly latch her baby onto the breast. A mother who is feeding all day will not be able to find time to eat or rest properly either. This would not be a good start to breastfeeding.

If you are bottle-feeding and trying to feed on demand you will end up with a sink full of half-drunken bottles, a very time-consuming and expensive exercise. And making a lot more than you really need could leave you tired or in too much of a hurry to wash, clean and sterilise the bottles properly, possibly resulting in your baby getting a tummy bug.

So, as you may have guessed, I feel that in today's society with less family support, it is too hard for most new parents to learn the skill of interpreting their baby's cries early enough to demand feed.

Teaching bad habits

If you feed your baby every time he cries, you run the risk of teaching him that the answer to all his emotional ups and downs is to eat, irrespective of whether he is actually hungry. For example, if a baby is tired and crying because he doesn't know how to put himself to sleep, feeding him teaches that he needs to eat in order to fall asleep. If a bored and crying baby is picked up and fed, he starts to understand that if he is bored then eating will help. If a baby is crying because he is too hot or too cold and is fed instead, he learns that he will feel better if he eats.

My problem with this is that as your baby turns into a toddler, his whingeing will see you starting to replace bottles or breastfeeds with a piece of fruit or a biscuit which reinforces the regime of feeding him when he cries. Perhaps this is one of the reasons why we now see a lot of obesity in children and teenagers and why others eat to solve emotional imbalance.

I don't want to infer that demand feeding won't work for everyone. In the end, all parents have to do what is best for them and if you are one of the lucky ones who can interpret your baby's cries, that's great; continue to feed on demand when the baby is telling you he is hungry. But be well aware that it is not always hunger that makes a baby cry and while a feed may temporarily quieten the baby, it is not always solving the problem.

BREAST, BOTTLE OR BOTH

Over the years I have come across lots of different approaches to feeding a new baby and there are advantages and disadvantages with them all. I have also found that whether a baby is breastfed or bottle-fed makes no difference to when they start sleeping through the night (when I say sleeping through the night I mean sleeping from 7 pm to 7 am with a dreamfeed at around 10 pm).

The decision of how you are going to feed your baby should be yours and yours only. Try not to listen to all the opinions people will give you. If you are still not sure when the baby arrives then why not try breastfeeding? You can always change your mind and formula-feed if it's not for you or your baby. But once formula-feeding, it would be difficult to change your mind a few weeks down the track as your milk may have dried up. If you do change your mind, contact your local breastfeeding association who can advise you on how to try to get your milk in again.

I get hundreds of emails and phone calls each year from parents who have been solely breastfeeding and, for one reason or another, have to introduce a bottle. Some of the reasons for needing to do so include a mother having to return to work, be admitted to hospital, or just needing an evening out every so often. Unfortunately, when left to a late stage, the struggle to get the baby to take a bottle can be a big one. Many mothers would like to continue breastfeeding in the morning and at night but when their baby finally takes the bottle they are too scared to reintroduce the breast in case the baby refuses the bottle again. If, in these circumstances, the baby had had a bottle a day from the early weeks, instead of giving up the breast altogether at four months the baby could have enjoyed both breast and bottle-feeding until maybe as late as two years old.

There are other benefits in giving your baby one bottle a day of either expressed breastmilk or formula. It gives the baby's father a chance to bond if they can give their baby a feed and, if this feed is done at night, it means the mother can have several hours of uninterrupted sleep. I have never found this to have any effect on a baby's ability to breastfeed or to a mother's milk supply, but I am also careful to include only one of these bottle-feeds in a 24-hour period.

HOW TO FEED YOUR BABY

Regardless of whether you are breastfeeding or bottle-feeding your baby, there are a few basic guidelines to follow:

- Always find somewhere comfortable and safe to sit, relax and enjoy the feed. Avoid feeding your baby in your bed, even during the early days in hospital, as you risk falling asleep and your baby having an accident.

- Have a cushion or pillow to rest your arm on as during the feed your baby will start to feel heavy. It will also help to get your baby in the correct position.

- Try to avoid interruptions such as phone calls.

- If you have an older child, introduce something special that they only do at feed times, for example, a bag of special toys or a DVD. This will both help to entertain them and to avoid feeling jealous of the time you are spending with their new sibling.

BREASTFEEDING

All experts agree that breastfeeding is the best and most natural way to feed your baby. Here's why:

- Breastmilk is fresh, clean and at the perfect temperature for your baby to drink.

- Breastmilk contains the complete balance of nutrients and antibodies that your baby needs to grow and develop and to protect him from illness.

- Breastmilk is also known to foster optimum brain growth.

- Breastmilk is easiest for your baby to digest and breastfed babies rarely get constipated.

- Babies who are fed only breastmilk until six months are at less risk from conditions such as asthma, eczema, allergies and food intolerance.

- Breastfed babies may also be less likely to develop coeliac disease or juvenile diabetes. There is also some current research that suggests breastfeeding may reduce the incidence of heart disease in later life.

- Best of all, this remarkable food is free!

There are also benefits for a breastfeeding mother:

- Hormones secreted during breastfeeding help keep you calm and also help with weight loss.

- Breastfeeding helps your uterus get back to its normal size and delays the return of menstruation.

- Some research indicates breastfeeding reduces the risks of developing pre-menopausal cancer of the breast, cervix and ovaries and also that women who breastfeed are less likely to suffer from osteoporosis and heart disease in later life.

However, breastfeeding is a learned skill for both mother and baby alike. Like childbirth, it helps to learn as much as you can before your baby arrives. With time, practise and support, most women can breastfeed successfully. There are plenty of people who will help you establish breastfeeding and a number of helpful books dedicated to the subject. After delivery, your midwife will encourage you to put your baby straight to the breast and guide you through the techniques of positioning and latching on. If you come out of hospital still not sure what to do, there are various organisations, such as La Leche League and The Breastfeeding Network, who have counsellors and other breastfeeding mothers who can talk to you and give you advice.

The four-hour routine

When my mother was born, most women had their baby in a hospital and sometimes stayed for as long as two weeks. In those days, breastfeeding was not encouraged and if you wanted to do so you had to follow the same guidelines as the mothers who were bottle-feeding their babies. Your baby was put onto a strict four-hour routine which, in my mother's case, was 6 am, 10 am, 2 pm, 6 pm, 10 pm and only one feed was allowed in the night at 2 am. Unfortunately, by the time my grandmother and other new mothers in her generation left hospital, their milk had well and truly dried up. I believe this is why in the fifties, sixties and even the seventies most babies were bottle-fed.

The main problem with feeding a breastfed newborn on a four-hour routine is that only six feeds a day will not stimulate your nipples enough to encourage a good milk supply. Most newborn babies don't have enough energy to take long feeds; they need to feed little and frequently and restricting their feeds to six in a 24-hour period may not be giving them their full daily requirements.

Breastfeeding before your milk comes in

The key to successful breastfeeding in the first two weeks is to stimulate the breasts frequently and encourage them to make enough milk by feeding your new baby little and often. Your breasts do not produce milk as soon as your baby is born; for the first couple of days, and sometimes before your baby is born, your breasts produce colostrum. This is a clear yellow-coloured fluid which is very good for your baby; it is full of antibodies and immunity-promoting cells. You will know when your milk is coming in because your breasts will feel warm, harder and fuller.

I advise my clients whose babies are born at full term and weight (2.75 kg / 6.1 lb) or more) to offer breastfeeds of six minutes on each side every three hours in the first 24 hours. On the second day, offer him nine minutes on each breast every three hours, and on the third day (if your milk has not come in yet) offer him twelve minutes on each side every three hours. On the fourth day, if your milk is still not in, give him sixteen minutes on each breast. This also means waking your baby in the middle of the night until your milk comes in.

Feeding three hourly not only builds up your milk supply but also helps your nipples get used to feeding, 'toughening' them up and helping avoid cracked, sore or bleeding nipples, which can be horribly painful.

Use the times in my guide below for the length of feeds in the early days, then once your milk has come in until your baby is two weeks old, use the times on the one to two week routine.

A GUIDE TO BREASTFEEDING BEFORE YOUR MILK COMES IN

	Right breast	Left breast
Day one: feed every three hours from both breasts	**6 minutes**	**6 minutes**
Day two: feed every three hours from both breasts	**9 minutes**	**9 minutes**
Day three: feed every three hours from both breasts (if milk not in)	**12 minutes**	**12 minutes**
Day four: feed every three hours from both breasts (if milk not in)	**16 minutes**	**16 minutes**

Let-down reflex

The let-down reflex is a normal part of breastfeeding that every mother will experience. During let-down, hormones called prolactin and oxytocin control the reflex and allow the milk produced in the milk glands, which is stored in milk sacs, to be released into the milk ducts.

All women find that their milk let-down is slightly different. Some women find just looking at their baby or hearing their baby cry causes the let-down, other mothers find it a little harder and have to find a quiet place to relax for the let-down to take place. Factors which can interfere with the reflex such as pain, stress, and anxiety can result in the retention of milk within the milk sacs which can cause additional pain and anxiety. If you experience this try remedies such as drinking plenty of water, performing a gentle massage or applying heat to your breasts. If you continue to have problems you should talk to your midwife or doctor.

Normal side effects of the let-down reflex are:

- a tingling sensation
- prickling or even slight pain in your breasts
- milk leaking from the breast without your baby feeding
- cramping in your uterus.

Breastfeeding when your milk comes in

You will know as soon as your milk is coming in because your breasts will start to become fuller and harder. You will notice the colour of your milk changing from the yellow colostrum to a paler, slightly blue milky colour. Some women suffer from painful engorged breasts at this time but this is less likely to happen if you are following my guide.

From the day your milk comes in, usually day three to five, you should offer your baby one breast until it is completely empty before offering the second breast. If you move your baby onto the second breast too soon he may not be getting enough hindmilk, which is the main reason some babies never seem satisfied after a feed. It may take up to 25 minutes for your baby to empty your breast. It is very important to feed every three hours during the day in the first two weeks. If you feed more often your baby may be snacking and never reaching that very important hindmilk.

After your milk has come in, you can let your baby sleep up to five hours at night in the first two weeks. But wake him at the five-hour mark as it could affect your milk supply if your breasts go too long at night without been stimulated.

> **Tip:** Work out the time between feeds from when the last feed began, not ended. So, if you start feeding your baby at 7 am but he finishes the feeding at 8 am, start the next feed at 10 am.

How to tell if your breast is empty

It is not always possible to be certain if your breast is empty but there are certain signs to look for.

If you gently squeeze your breast at the beginning of a feed you will notice it feels firm. This is a full breast. As the feed progresses, your breast will become softer and feel less full and when your breast is just about empty it will feel quite soft. Watch your baby at the beginning of the feed; he will be sucking strongly with almost no pauses. When he reaches the point where the breast is nearly empty he will take big pauses in his sucking.

My routines may specify fifteen or 25 minutes for a feed, but if you are sure your baby has emptied your breast sooner than this then move him to the next breast.

Expressing

Before having a baby, parents often have an idea of what they plan to do. Most parents decide after reading my advice they are going to breastfeed and give one bottle of expressed milk a day, or whenever they find it not convenient to breastfeed. Unfortunately, once the baby is born, this doesn't always pan out. By the time you fit in feeding, changing, settling and maybe even a quick shower for you, there is no time left for expressing. But I cannot overemphasise how important expressing is during the first few weeks if you are trying to establish breastfeeding while following one of my routines.

The reason for this is that breastmilk is produced on a supply-and-demand basis. At first you will have much more milk than your baby needs but after a few days your breasts will start to regulate and produce only the amount he is taking. This is fine initially, but when your baby goes through a growth spurt in the early weeks you may not have enough milk to satisfy his needs. This would result in you having to feed him more often and will get your routine off track and may also result in you feeding your baby too close to sleep time resulting in him using the feed as a going-to-sleep aid.

Mothers who follow my advice and express their extra milk in the early days find that when their baby goes through a growth spurt, the routine they are following stays intact. I strongly believe that expressing in the early days is the key factor in having a good milk supply while following a routine. The good thing about expressing on a routine is you should have no problem getting your milk out, as at the times I suggest you express you will have plenty of milk.

The best time to express is first thing in the morning because your breasts are usually fuller at this point. Some mothers find it easier to express before they get their baby up in the morning; others find feeding their baby on one breast while expressing the other easier. Expressing before a feed will also give your breastmilk more time to build up for the next feed.

In the first few weeks I suggest expressing at other times in the day as well as first thing in the morning (these times are explained later along with the routines). Expressing in the morning may take around twenty minutes but in the evening it can take up to 35 minutes. It is usually easier to express if you are relaxed. Sometimes a bit of encouragement is needed to assist the let-down in the evening: a warm bath or shower can help, or try a very gentle massage before you begin. Expressing does get easier with practise.

How to express

I encourage all my clients to express first thing in the morning and at other times in the day. This is for two reasons. One, this milk can be given in the bottle later in the day and some of it can be frozen and stored for when your baby has a growth spurt. Two, your breasts are fuller in the morning. I highly recommend an electric pump for most of my mums as the hand-held ones are very slow at getting the milk out. You can hire these electric breast-pumps from some chemists and from your local breastfeeding association.

The first thing you will need to do is to find somewhere comfortable to sit and relax. You will need to stimulate your let-down. Do this by spending a minute stroking the breast you are going to express from very gently, working from the top of your breast towards the nipple. After a few minutes, use your thumb and third finger to gently squeeze the areola (the skin around your nipple), squeezing and releasing until you see drops of milk appear. Once this happens you should start to use an electric breast-pump to express your milk. There is no reason why you can't go straight onto the pump without stimulating your breast first, but it may take a lot longer to get your milk flowing.

If you can't express

Some mothers' breasts produce just enough for their baby and no extra and cannot express. If this happens to you, don't panic. You will just need to be careful in the first seven weeks that your baby is not hungry due to a growth spurt. If you believe he is hungry between feeds and you have no expressed milk, just offer an extra feed for a few days no closer than two and a half hours after the last one. If you are not expressing you can use my routines as guides until week eight. At week eight you can follow my routines to the minute because expressing is not required to make the routine work successfully.

Storage of breastmilk

Freshly expressed breastmilk can be stored in a closed sterile container or in a breastmilk freezer bag at room temperature for four hours, but it is better to store it in the fridge or freezer. It can be stored in the fridge for three to five days; try to place it at the back, which is normally colder. You can store it in the freezer compartment of the fridge for up to two weeks, in a freezer with a separate door for up to three months and in a deep freezer for up to six months (–18°C or lower).

After taking breastmilk out of the freezer, it is best to defrost it in the fridge. You can store it in the fridge for up to 24 hours. If defrosted at room temperature, it needs to be used within four hours. Never refreeze breastmilk. If you need the breastmilk sooner, you can sit the container or bag in a little bit of warm (not boiling) water, but use it straight away.

Never reuse bottled fresh or defrosted breastmilk after the feed is finished. If you are not sure how much your baby will drink, start out with less in the bottle and top up with milk stored in the fridge or freezer if required.

BOTTLE-FEEDING

Like breastfeeding, bottle-feeding is a learned skill for both you and your baby. It is not as simple as buying some bottles, filling them with breastmilk or formula and feeding your baby when he seems hungry, but unfortunately, not as much help and advice is readily available to parents who are learning how to bottle-feed.

There are a few questions you need to address before you start bottle-feeding:

- Which bottles or teats are best for your baby?

- Are you going to bottle-feed with expressed milk, formula or a combination of both expressed milk and formula?
- Which formula is best for your baby?

Bottles and teats

Choosing the right bottle for your baby is a very important factor in how happy and satisfied your bottle-fed baby will be. I suggest you buy two types of bottles to start with: one short, fat one with a wide neck (for example, the Avent brand) and the other a tall, thin bottle with a flattened orthodontic teat (for example, a Tommee Tippee first feeding bottle).

Some people prefer the wide-necked bottles as they are easier to make up feeds with. Most baby bottles leak but from my experience, the bottles that leak actually seem to work better by reducing the amount of air your baby takes in.

Teats come in all shapes and sizes, with different flows such as slow, medium and fast. Some have a variable teat which covers all ages and is controlled by which part is pointing to your baby's nose.

Don't underestimate how important it is to find the right bottle and teat for your baby as some babies can have difficult experiences with one that doesn't suit them.

> **Tip:** When buying your baby a bottle, check the teat size. Most bottles come with medium teats so you will also need a newborn teat with a slow flow.

Alannah's story

When I went to visit baby Alannah, she had been crying for the six weeks since she had been born. Her parents were worried sick and could not work out what was wrong with her. Their three older children had their moments as babies but never cried for more than twenty minutes at this young age. But Alannah seemed to cry nearly eighteen hours out of every 24. The rest of the time she was sleeping, but never for more than twenty minutes at one time. Like most cases, I was met by two very tired parents, Cathy and Baz, and I soon found out what a horrid few weeks they had gone through.

Cathy had started off breastfeeding but after a week of constant crying and a visit from a lactation consultant who couldn't find a problem, Alannah was switched to formula in case it was a hunger problem. As this had made no difference after another week, they went down the reflux and medication path. When that made no difference, it was 'maybe Alannah has an allergy, let's try different formulas'. So by the time I arrived, Alannah was on prescription formula and medication for reflux. She had also seen a paediatrician specialising in infant reflux, but he could only prescribe different medication and formulas.

Taking Alannah in my arms and feeling her back and very gently squeezing under her rib cage, I found she was full of wind. I sat with her for about an hour and got most of the wind up then decided to feed her. When I tried to feed Alannah from the bottle they were using, I showed Cathy and Baz how Alannah's chin was the problem. It was set back slightly, so latching on to this particular bottle was not going to work. I explained to them that Alannah would have had the same problem with the breast but, if they had stopped every few minutes and winded her, she would have brought the wind up and been able to take bigger feeds, been more satisfied and not cried all the time.

Next we switched Alannah to a tall, thin bottle with a flattened orthodontic teat which reduced the amount of air she was swallowing. Alannah took a full feed, fell asleep and spent the next four days feeding and sleeping with very little awake time.

Before starting a bottle-feed, make sure the screw ring on the top of the bottle that holds the teat in place is not too tight, otherwise the milk will not come out easily and him could get tired of sucking too soon. When you are giving him a bottle, hold your baby in a slightly more upright position than when breastfeeding. This will help him not to choke on the milk if it flows out too fast and it will also help him to bring up wind as he feeds. You should always watch the teat to make sure it is full of milk so that your baby does not take in too much air.

Young babies should be allowed to take as long as 40 minutes to one hour for a full feed, including winding time. I advise starting by winding your baby every 30 ml (1 oz) and, if you see no signs of discomfort in him, in the evening increase the amount of milk you give him before you stop to wind. (This is explained in greater detail in the next chapter under winding and colic.) Your baby should be sucking at a slow and steady pace, so you will need to experiment with the different teats to find the flow that suits him. Babies get great pleasure from sucking and if the feed is over too fast your baby may start crying, not because he is hungry but because he wants to continue to suck. So don't put a faster teat on to make the feed take less time. When your baby is ten weeks the feed may take as little as 30 minutes, and by six months a feed should be about twenty minutes.

Warming a bottle

Warming breastmilk

Warm expressed breastmilk by standing the bottle or bag of milk in warm water – not boiling water, as the milk might curdle or the bag may melt. Never warm or thaw breastmilk in a microwave oven, as I mention on the next page as the milk heats unevenly and may also change the immunological and nutrient quality of breastmilk.

Warming formula

There is no reason not to feed your baby cold formula straight out of the fridge and if you do so from the start, he will not know the difference. However, I always warm milk up for babies as I believe they prefer it, although on a really hot summer day some babies may like their milk cold. You can heat formula by:

- Standing the bottle of mixed formula in hot (not boiling) water.
- Using a thermostatically controlled bottle warmer.

I do not recommend using a microwave to heat breastmilk or formula for a baby. Microwaves can cause heat spots in the milk and this could burn him. They are also thought to change the quality of breastmilk so I would worry about what it could do to formula. Instead of heating the pre-mixed formula I suggest heating the correct amount of water and then adding the powdered formula to this. After shaking the water and formula to mix it the hot spots should go.

The above methods all work perfectly well, but the most important thing is to check the temperature of the formula before you give it to your baby. Do this by shaking a few drops from the teat onto your wrist; it should feel warm but not hot. Overheating formula not only risks burning your baby but could also destroy some of the nutrients in the milk. It is far better to give the milk slightly cool rather than too hot.

Tip: It is well worthwhile varying the temperature of the milk as some babies can become fussy and start to refuse feeds unless the milk is at a particular temperature.

Bottle-feeding with expressed milk

After ten weeks you will be able to follow my routines without doing any expressing. If you would like to keep giving your baby a bottle of expressed milk then I suggest you express at the same feed every day so your breasts know when the extra milk is needed. I suggest this is at the 7 am and 11 am feeds each day.

Some mothers find themselves in the situation where, even though they are producing enough milk, breastfeeding is difficult and they are advised for one reason or another to bottle-feed their baby. If this is because you are taking medication which may affect your baby through your breastmilk then it makes sense to put him on formula. But if you have been advised that your milk is perfectly safe for your baby then it could be worth trying to express and give your baby breastmilk from a bottle. In these cases, sometimes mothers find they just don't have enough time in the day to express milk for all their baby's feeds, but some breastmilk is better than none. If you are mixed feeding, never put the expressed breastmilk and formula in the bottle together: give the breastmilk first and, when the bottle is empty, put in some formula to finish the feed (or use two different bottles). It is not dangerous to mix formula with breastmilk but it is a shame to waste breastmilk and it might not taste very nice together.

While establishing breastfeeding in the first ten weeks, it is very important to not go too long without feeding or expressing. You will notice in my routines that if I suggest giving your baby a bottle of expressed milk, I also say when next to express. If you choose to give him a bottle of expressed milk at other times then you need to follow these guidelines:

- From when your baby is born until he is two weeks and over 3 kg (6.6 lb), don't go more than five hours without feeding or expressing during any 24-hour period.

- From two weeks until four weeks, don't go longer than six hours in any 24-hour period without expressing or feeding.

- From four to ten weeks, you can let your breast go any length of time between 10.30 pm and 7 am but don't go any longer than six hours during the day without feeding from the breast or expressing.

Bottle-feeding with formula

While breastmilk is undoubtedly the best milk you can give your baby, formula is the next best thing. Most infant formulas are based on cow's milk which is then modified to bring it closer to the composition of breastmilk; others are based on soya milk or goat's milk. All formulas on the market must comply with the relevant food standards code. These are based on expert recommendations and regulate ingredients, manufacturing and labelling. The composition of infant formulas is constantly being improved with advances in technology and nutrition science, so it really is the next safest thing for your baby.

Choosing a suitable formula for your baby can be very confusing. If you decide to formula-feed in hospital, you will be given advice on which formula to use, how to sterilise the bottles and how to prepare a feed. If it is at a later stage that you decide to formula-feed, there are a few things to be aware of. Some formulas are suitable from birth until you wean your baby onto cow's milk, others are suitable from birth to six months with a follow-on formula from six months onwards. Some parents need to choose their baby's formula based on religious beliefs, for example, a kosher diet.

There are lots of little differences, such as whether it contains long-chain fatty acids, nucleotides or probiotics.

TYPES OF FORMULA

Types of Formula	Description
Cow's milk-based formula	This is either whey-dominant or curd-dominant. It will tell you on the tin which it is. Both types of formula are suitable for your baby from birth. The whey-predominant ones are preferable, as they are closer to breastmilk. Some formulas have added omega 3 and omega 6 fatty acids that may assist in brain and visual development.
Soy-based formula	Often given to babies with an allergy or an intolerance to the protein found in cow's milk. Sometimes it is given to a baby on a lactose-free diet, but there are other lactose-free formulas available. It is also suitable for a baby under twelve months of age as an alternative to cow's milk formula. It is not the same as soya milk, as your baby needs it in formula style.
Goat's milk-based formula	Suitable for babies under twelve months of age as an alternative to cow's or soy-based formula. Often, babies who have an allergy or intolerance to cow's milk-based formulas, have the same reactions to goat's milk-based formulas, as the two formulas are very similar. Again, it has to be given in formula style, as it is not the same as normal goat's milk.
Low-lactose/lactose-free formula	Given to babies who are lactose intolerant. You should consult your health professional before choosing to put your baby on low-lactose or lactose-free formula.

Thickened formula	Suitable for babies with gastro-oesophageal reflux. It is usually thickened with a baby-friendly food thickener such as carob bean flour. The need for thickened formula should be reviewed regularly with your health professional.
Hypoallergenic formula	Given to babies with severe allergies or food intolerances. There are some that can be bought off the shelf and others for more severe cases, which are available by prescription only.
Follow-on formula	Given to babies over six months. It contains increased levels of iron, calcium and sometimes protein.
Ready-made formula	These are becoming more common. They are a very expensive option but well worth the investment, if you are short of time. They come in a handy one-feed size, as they can be kept at room temperature until opened. They are also a good option if you are asking someone else to look after your baby, as they will have more time to enjoy him.

How to prepare formula

In the past it has been recommended that formula could be made up in a jug in bulk for a 24-hour period; however, please be aware this has now changed. Recent research has shown that formula should only be made up in individual bottles directly before the feed time. You should try to donate one part of your work surface to bottle preparing and keep this area extra clean.

- First wash your hands with warm, soapy water.

- Always empty and rinse out your kettle before filling it with fresh water for bottle preparation.

- Fill the kettle with water from your cold water tap and boil it. Tip into a sterilised jug and leave on the worktop to cool.

- Fill the bottles with the correct amount of boiled water. Always make up a little more formula than you expect your baby to drink. Seal the bottles or jug before leaving them to cool.

- Allow the water to sit and cool for a minimum of twenty minutes. This will mean the water will be hot but not boiling. Boiling water will kill some of the nutrients in the formula. If you are in a hurry you can sit the sealed bottle in a saucepan of cold water.

- Add the formula powder to the water; check the tin for your formula's guidelines. Some powders are one scoop to 30 ml (1 oz) but some are one scoop to 60 ml (2 oz). All are measured with a level scoop, so you need to gently scrape the powder off the top of the scoop.

- Dissolve the powder by putting the lid on your bottle and giving it a good shake until you see all the formula has dissolved.

- If you need to warm the milk to feed your baby, either stand the bottle in a jug with some hot (not boiling) water or place your bottle in a thermostatically controlled bottle warmer.

If you do not have time to cool the boiled water from the kettle, or if you prefer not to boil the kettle for each feed, you can keep a jug of boiled water on the worktop at room temperature or in the fridge for no longer than 24 hours, and fill your bottles for preparation from this. Please remember to empty, sterilise and refill the jug every 24 hours.

How much should I feed my baby?

Every baby will vary in the amount of milk they take. I have also found the feeding guides on the side of formula tins to be very different to the amount I have ever given a baby. It is much easier to underfeed a baby than overfeed, so a useful rule is to always have some liquid left in the bottle: if your baby drains the bottle, offer some more. (Unless, of course, you notice your baby bringing up a lot of milk after every feed – if this happens I suggest you cut back on the amount of milk by 10 ml (0.3 oz)and see if the vomiting stops. If not cut it by a further 10 ml (0.3 oz)at the next feed. You should also read my possetting advice on pages 51–52 and advice on vomiting and dehydration on pages 249–251.)

This is a rough guide as every baby is slightly different. The amount of formula your baby needs is usually worked out by his body weight. Take your baby's weight and multiply it by the recommended amount of formula for his age group, then divide it by the amount of feeds you are giving in a 24-hour period. For example, if your baby is 3.5 kg (7.7 lb) and one week old, he needs 3.5 × 150 ml = 525 ml (7.7 × 2.3 oz = 17.71 oz) in a 24-hour period. If he is having eight feeds a day, divide 525 ml by 8 = 65.60 ml (17.71 oz by 8 = 2.21 oz) per feed. Therefore, your baby will have roughly 65 ml (2.2 oz) per feed. But some babies drink a lot more than what is recommended and some drink a lot less. Try not to get too worried about how much your baby is having – if he has plenty of wet nappies, is putting on enough weight and your health professional is happy, then you should be too.

HOW MUCH TO FORMULA-FEED: A ROUGH GUIDE

Age of baby	Amount of formula per feed	Number of formula feeds in 24 hours
Birth to one week	30–90 ml (1–3 oz)	Eight feeds
One to two weeks	150 ml per kg (2.3 oz per pound) of body weight ÷ number of feeds	Eight feeds
Two to four weeks	150 ml per kg (2.3 oz per pound) of body weight ÷ number of feeds	Seven to eight feeds
Four to six weeks	150 ml per kg (2.3 oz per pound) of body weight ÷ number of feeds	Six to eight feeds
Six to eight weeks	150 ml per kg (2.3 oz per pound) of body weight ÷ number of feeds	Six to seven feeds
Eight weeks until baby is on solids	150 ml per kg (2.3 oz per pound) of body weight ÷ number of feeds	Five to six feeds
A baby on solids until nine months	180–240 ml (6–8 oz)	Four feeds
Nine months to one year	120–210 ml (4–7 oz)	Two full feeds and two half feeds (three feeds in total)

Over the years I have been called out hundreds of times to see babies who spend hours and hours screaming. Usually I am told the same thing by the parents: they will only sleep for very short periods, up to twenty minutes at a time. Most have seen various paediatricians and other health professionals but no one has been able to interpret what the babies are crying about. These sorts of cases are very upsetting, because it is as though no one sees the obvious while looking for some big problem. Usually, by the time I am called, the babies have been put on various formulas and medications, all of which could have been avoided if someone had sat back and listened to what the baby was trying to say – 'I'm hungry!'

After explaining to the parents why I would like to feed their baby more, I am told over and over again that they can't because their health professional advised only giving their baby a set amount of formula at each feed, and their baby has just had that set amount. (In my eyes, this is putting a newborn infant on a diet. Has the world really gone this crazy?)

In all of these cases, the parents will be giving their baby anything from 120 to 150 ml (4 oz to 5 oz) per feed. I pick the screaming baby up, introduce myself and feed him a further 120 to 150 ml (4 oz to 5 oz). The parents often sit in shock and look at how much their baby is drinking. I explain that he will not drink this large amount of formula at every feed: if, for example, he has been allowed only 120 ml (4 oz) per feed, after a few very large feeds the baby will settle down to 150 ml (5 oz) per feed. The other common factor in most of these cases is that the babies are constipated. I believe this is because there was not enough milk going in to push the poo out.

David's story

One case which always sticks in my mind is David's, who was two weeks old at the time of my visit. His health visitor had put him on a diet of 120 ml (4 oz)of formula at each feed and in fact visited at the same time I did. As she didn't know who I was or why I was there, I asked her for myself: 'What happens if he is screaming for more food after the 120 ml (4 oz)?' I was shocked when she told me, 'At two weeks old, 120 ml (4 oz) is all he is allowed.' I did as I described above and fed him a lot more formula and as a result we soon had a very contented sleeping baby.

The strangest part was when David's father came in the door from work – I saw he was 6'11! Yet David's health visitor put him on the same diet as all the other two-week-old babies on her books.

STERILISING

Whether breastfeeding or bottle-feeding, you will still need to understand the importance of disinfecting, usually referred to as 'sterilising'. Young babies have immature immune systems and are very susceptible to bacteria. Milk is a perfect medium for bacteria to multiply in so sterilising is the best way to ensure they are destroyed.

Health professionals usually recommend you sterilise all your baby's feeding equipment, including any breast-pump parts, until your baby is at least six months. You can't sterilise everything that goes into your baby's mouth, of course (for example, you don't need to sterilise your nipple!) However, anything that is not getting sterilised needs to be washed carefully first. Get into the habit of washing your hands after every nappy change, even if your baby is screaming. You can still put him down in a safe place for a minute to wash your hands. If a dummy falls out of your baby's mouth into his bed or pram, it's fine to put it back into his mouth, but if it falls on the floor or street, it should be washed thoroughly in hot soapy water first. Most dummies cannot be sterilised as they start to fall apart – another good reason not to use them! Please be aware that having a suck on it yourself will not clean or sterilise it, you are just adding germs to it.

Anything that comes in contact with the milk you give your baby, such as bottles, teats and breast-pump parts, should be sterilised to ensure there are no traces of bacteria left. If there was some bacteria left in a bottle, for example, and your baby's milk was added to it, the bacteria could multiply. This could cause your baby to have a minor tummy upset, which won't do much harm except unsettle him and disrupt your routine. However, more serious bugs such as gastroenteritis can be dangerous in young babies and may even result in being admitted to hospital.

Sterilising is not a substitute for washing. Everything you sterilise first needs to be washed thoroughly. After using a bottle or breast-pump, rinse milk off in cold water and then leave it to one side for proper washing later. Make sure you pull each bit of the equipment apart, taking teats out of the screw rings on the top of bottles, for example. Wash each part very thoroughly in hot, soapy water, using a bottle-brush for the inside of bottles. Squirt a bit of washing-up liquid on the teats and wash all around them, squeezing some water through the hole. Rinse the soap off with hot water and place everything in the steriliser, or on a clean drying rack, or dry with some paper towels or a clean cloth.

There are four main methods of sterilisation:

1 Boiling all the equipment for ten minutes in a large saucepan.

2 Soaking in a sterilising solution, bought in liquid or tablet form from chemists and some supermarkets, for a minimum of two hours, then rinsing equipment with boiling water after you remove it. Even if you are using a different form of sterilising, it is handy to have some solution as a back-up.

3 Microwave sterilisers turn water into steam in the microwave and take approximately three to four minutes.

4 Electric steam sterilisers usually take all shaped bottles, but remember to check yours will fit first. They take approximately seven minutes from start to finish.

I have tried and tested all of these methods of sterilisation and would recommend the electric steam steriliser above all the others if you can afford it. The microwave versions do not hold as many bottles and I worry about microwaving plastic bottles over and over again, but if you have glass bottles this would not be a concern.

I don't recommend using a dishwasher to sterilise as they vary in temperature so you can't be sure if you are really doing the job.

> **Tip:** Bottles and other equipment may be wet after you take them out of some sterilisers, but the insides of bottles do not need to be dry before putting milk into them.

COMMON QUESTIONS

Should you watch what you eat while breastfeeding?
There are so many 'old wives' tales' out there about what you can and can't eat or drink while breastfeeding, and I must say I have never found any truth in them. I believe you can pretty much eat what you like while breastfeeding unless your family or your partner's family have a history of an allergic reaction to a particular food, such as peanuts. If there is, avoid that food. And it's best to avoid alcohol altogether while pregnant and breastfeeding.

Is it true that small-breasted woman just can't breastfeed? I have actually found more problems with large-breasted women trying to breastfeed, while many small-breasted women find breastfeeding easy. Most women can breastfeed but it is a learned skill. If you are having problems, ask for advice before you give up.

Can I breastfeed and take medication? There are very few medicines that can't be taken safely while breastfeeding, but always ask your health professional about any medication, including herbal supplements and medications bought over the counter. Never take the combined pill while breastfeeding as this will cause your breastmilk to dry up. If you decide to take the mini pill, keep a close eye on your baby's feeds as sometimes it changes the taste of your milk, which could cause him to drink less and less until your milk is gone.

What can I do if my baby keeps falling asleep on the breast before I can empty it? Always make sure your baby is fully awake before you try to feed him. One way to wake your baby is to unswaddle him. Take the bottom half of his clothes off and let him wake up slowly. Try to keep a sleepy baby cooler while feeding as this will help to keep him awake. If he falls asleep while feeding on the second breast, this is all right and you should put him back to bed. However, if it is the first breast, take him off the breast and let him have a five-minute sleep, then talk to him and try to encourage him to wake again. If no luck, put him down on his playmat and finish the feed when he wakes up. You may find you have to do this every few minutes until the first breast is finished.

Does exercise affect breastmilk? It is thought that some physical exercise such as jogging or running should be avoided while breastfeeding, as lactic acid builds up in the milk and affects the taste. Light physical activities such as walking will make you feel better and will not affect your breastmilk. Some babies don't like the taste of sweat or chlorine so you might be better to take a shower before breastfeeding if you notice a problem.

Are some babies too big to breastfeed? The fact is that almost all mothers and babies work as a team to make just the right amount of breastmilk needed. Whether your baby was born early or was the biggest baby in hospital history, your breastmilk will match his needs.

Should I offer my baby water to drink? Babies under two months should not be given supplemental water, unless you are concerned your baby is suffering from constipation or dehydration. If that is the case, only give water in very small amounts (about 30 ml / 1 oz) between milk feeds. For a baby over two months, too much water can fill him up so that he nurses less. Babies need the nutrition and calories in breastmilk or formula to grow – water has none of these. When your four- to six-month-old baby is learning to use a cup, giving him a few sips of water a couple of times a day is fine and fun. Once your baby starts solids, you might want to give him a few sips of water with his solids – some babies need this to prevent constipation.

My baby will often only take one breast and then won't want the other side. If I don't express the other side so that I am comfortable my supply seems to go down within a few days, right when he

wants to feed from both sides all day! Should I take him off one side halfway through the feed and swap him over, or will I get mastitis from not draining my breast properly? You should definitely not take him off halfway through the feed and change sides or he will not be getting enough of the hindmilk which babies need the most. It is perfectly normal for your baby not to take both sides at each feed. If you follow my expressing advice and 'rotate' your breasts so each is drained every other feed, you should avoid mastitis.

How long can I use one bottle of formula for? From when you put a bottle of formula in your baby's mouth, you can use it for one hour. If after one hour he has not finished what is in the bottle, throw it out and get a fresh bottle. Untouched formula can only be reheated once.

When powdered formula is added to 240 ml (8 oz) of water in a bottle so that it measures 270 ml (9 oz), is this defined as 240 ml (8 oz) or 270 ml (9 oz) of formula? This is a common question. I have always called it 270 ml (9 oz) because if you were pouring it from a jug or using ready-made formula, this would be the case.

How long is a sterilised bottle sterile for? Well, the truth is, it is not sterile from the second you open the steriliser. Sterilising ensures that every last bit of old milk is removed to keep your baby as safe from bacteria as possible. It is recommended you fill and seal a bottle within an hour of sterilising and, if you don't, you should sterilise it again.

Will my baby sleep through the night sooner if formula-fed? Many parents falsely believe if they formula-feed their baby it will be easier to establish a routine and he will be sleeping through the night sooner than if they breastfeed. The fact is, formula-feeding alone will not produce a happy, sleeping baby; I have just as many bottle-feeding parents contact me as breastfeeding ones. Some parents choose to bottle-feed so other people can take on the responsibility of the night feeds, but you can still achieve this while breastfeeding by expressing at my recommended times and giving this milk during the night. Another thing I often hear is that breastfed babies have a stronger bond with their mothers. I do not believe this to be true. A baby has a strong bond with his parents the moment he is born and how your baby is fed is not a factor in how this bond develops.

Can I give my baby formula and breastmilk mixed? There is no reason you cannot (although it might taste a bit funny) but I would always recommend giving breastmilk first as it is better for him. It would be a real shame if the two were mixed and your baby did not finish the feed, meaning breastmilk is thrown out along with formula.

How do you work out the time between feeds? From when your baby's last feed started, not ended. So, if you started feeding him at 7 am but he finishes the feed at 8 am, you start the next feed three hours from the 7 am mark, so this would be 10 am.

What is mixed feeding? I define mixed feeding as when a baby is getting both breastmilk and formula. There are lots of different reasons for mixed feeding but it is very important to remember that even a very small amount of breastmilk is better than none, so mixed feeding should always be encouraged before you give up on breastfeeding altogether.

There are different combinations of mixed feeding. Some parents give breastmilk from the breast and formula to top up a feed: be careful with this as giving more than one bottle a day could affect your milk supply, or your baby may start to prefer the bottle and refuse to breastfeed if more than one bottle is given a day. Seek advice from your health professional before you give more than one bottle a day if you want to continue to breastfeed.

3

THINGS AFFECTING SLEEP AND SETTLING

Many factors can affect the way your baby settles and sleeps. If she is uncomfortable with wind, thrush, nappy rash or constipation, it will be very hard if not impossible for her to get to sleep. Or if your baby filled up on water, for example, she would be too hungry to sleep. This chapter covers some of the information I share with families on my home visits that will affect the way your baby settles to sleep.

BREAST REFUSAL

When a baby suddenly refuses to feed from the breast, many parents are surprised, upset and confused at what is happening. Mothers usually describe a baby who latches onto the breast and attempts to suck then pulls off and cries. There are a few common factors in these circumstances. Sometimes the refusal is because the baby is ill or there are too many distractions in the room you are trying to feed in. The first thing you should try if your baby is refusing the breast is to move into a quiet, maybe even darkened room, and try to feed her again. Never try to force your baby to take the breast as this will not help and, besides causing both you and your baby distress, could result in her never taking the breast again.

Sometimes the breast refusal happens 24 hours before a mother gets her first period after the birth with the baby refusing to feed for about eighteen hours. I believe this is because the breastmilk tastes different during this time. You will not know if this is the reason behind the breast refusal because your first period will only appear 24 hours after the refusal has started. The consolation is that this situation doesn't seem to occur with any further periods. However, regardless of why your baby is refusing the breast you should follow some safety guidelines.

If this happens and your baby is under eight weeks I advise seeking medical attention if she refuses to feed for more than twelve hours; if over eight weeks keep offering the breast and wait for her to start taking it again, but if feeds are refused for more than 24 hours seek medical advice. Avoid giving bottles of formula unless your doctor tells you to. At the times you would normally feed your baby express to keep up your milk supply.

Breast refusal also sometimes occurs when a mother has been on the mini pill for six weeks. As the mini pill only contains progesterone (and no oestrogen), it is thought not to affect milk supply, but I suspect the taste of the milk can sometimes be altered due to hormonal changes brought about by the mini pill. I advise mothers to stop taking the mini pill if they want to continue breastfeeding in these circumstances and the baby will usually go back to feeding normally within 48 hours. But if a mother has been on the mini pill longer than six weeks by the time she contacts me, the baby will often not go back on the breast as fast and their doctor may advise giving the baby some formula. Before long these babies may be fully formula-fed, so though this side effect may not be commonly heard of, it's something to be aware of if you choose the mini pill.

WINDING

Regardless of how or what you are feeding your baby, winding her is very important. Wind is caused by your baby taking in air while she is feeding and when this air accumulates in the tummy, you may end up with a very unsettled baby. Some babies seem to suffer more from wind than others.

I tell all my clients to start by winding their baby every 30 ml (1 oz) if bottle-feeding and every three minutes if breastfeeding. Watch how your baby responds to this in the evening. If there is no unsettled period, slowly increase the amount of milk you give her between winding. Spend a bit of extra time at the end of a feed winding, just to make sure all the air has come up. I also recommend that after each burp, during or at the end of a feed, you offer her some more milk.

To get the air bubbles up, have your baby's back as straight as possible. I find the easiest way to achieve this is to hold your baby on your lap, with one hand supporting her chin and under her arms, and pat or rub her back. Another way is to lay her head and arms over your shoulder and again pat or rub her back. If I can't get a burp up, I sometimes lay the baby down for a minute and then lift her up again. With the assistance of gravity, the burp often comes up.

Sometimes, if a baby is not winded often enough, the air comes up so fast that it brings some milk up first. If this is becoming a problem, try winding your baby more often. With a very young baby it can occasionally take up to fifteen minutes to get a burp up – I never give up until I get it! If you reward your baby for burping by putting her straight back on the breast or bottle, she will very quickly realise what you want and burp faster for you.

COLIC

Although much research on colic has been conducted, scientists have not been able to conclusively define it or to prove that there is indeed a condition. When I talk about colic in this book I am using it as a term to describe a pattern of unsettled behaviour and continuous crying in some babies in the first few months of their life. Statistically, colic seems to occur in about one in every five babies and is equally common in breastfed and formula-fed babies. I believe putting babies into a structured routine can counter the effect of colic and, if the routine is followed correctly, within 24 hours the crying often disappears.

Parents who contact me for help with their 'colicky' babies describe how the baby screams for hours at a time, usually in the evening. They also describe how their baby keeps bringing up their legs, as if in pain. I explain to them that I believe colic is often caused by the way we feed and wind our babies.

Imagine the stomach in six parts and picture it after each feed. Start from when your baby has had the longest sleep in a 24-hour period, say from 1 am until 6 am. At 6 am your baby has the first feed of the day. You wind your baby a few times during this feed, but not enough, although you may not realise this as you have heard a couple of big burps. Now imagine the baby's stomach is one-sixth wind and five-sixths milk. You settle the baby and all seems fine. At the next feed the same thing happens, but this time the stomach is two-sixths wind and four-sixths milk. And so on until the sixth feed. The baby's brain is telling her she is hungry but with her stomach five-sixths wind, she only has one-sixth left for food. You try feeding your hungry, crying baby but, after a minute, she can't fit any more food in. Consequently, the screaming starts for two reasons – first, hunger and second, the build-up of wind.

Taking the baby off the breast every three minutes or off the bottle every 30 ml (1 oz) to wind her may take a few minutes (and, if your baby is hungry, may result in some screaming), but a few minutes of crying while winding is better than a few hours later on. I advise parents not to feed the baby again until they get a burp up and to increase the time they allow the baby to feed between winding by a little each day. But if they see that the colic returns, they need to wind more frequently again.

Another common factor in the colicky babies I see is that they are demand-fed. Feeding this way all too often leads to the baby having another feed before the first one has been fully digested. My mantra again: *babies need a structured routine*.

HICCUPS

Hiccups are normal in a baby and often happen after a feed. I usually see them as a sign that the baby is full. Unlike adults, babies don't seem to be bothered by hiccups. If it is sleep time and your baby has hiccups, put her down as normal. Occasionally, some babies get upset by hiccups – if so, you could try giving some gripe water.

POSSETING/SMALL VOMITS

Some babies bring up a little milk after their feeds. This is called posseting. As previously mentioned, with some babies it is caused by not being winded enough during and after a feed. The extra air comes up so fast that it brings milk up ahead of it, sometimes even as a projectile vomit. In these cases, posseting can be lessened or stopped altogether by more attention being paid to winding your baby.

Posseting can look like a considerable amount of milk – even as though the whole feed has come up – but it won't be as much as it looks. If this happens occasionally and your baby is still gaining enough weight, you have nothing to worry about.

If your baby is not gaining weight and the posseting is becoming very frequent, your baby could be suffering from a condition called reflux and you should have her examined by your doctor.

Tip: If a baby of any age brings up all the milk from two feeds in a row, take your baby to a doctor straight away.

GASTRO-OESOPHAGEAL REFLUX

Often shortened to reflux, this condition affects many babies but frequently goes undiagnosed. Essentially, it is when the baby has a weaker sphincter muscle at the top of the stomach. The muscle is supposed to let food in but not let it back out of the stomach, but when it is weak it allows the contents of the stomach to go back up into the baby's oesophagus.

All babies are born with a weak sphincter muscle and many experience posseting (little vomits) as a result. This is perfectly normal and nothing to worry about if the baby seems to remain happy and is putting on weight. Other babies, however, become very uncomfortable as they can experience very painful burps and suffer in the way an adult would with acid heartburn.

Not all babies experience the same symptoms with reflux, sometimes making it difficult to diagnose. In some cases the baby suffers from the acid heartburn but also brings up a little or a lot of the milk (posseting) after a feed. In other cases, the reflux is 'silent' and is harder to diagnose because there is no posseting with the burps.

In very serious cases, the bottom part of the oesophagus becomes inflamed and if left untreated, inflammation and ulcers in the oesophagus can cause scarring. This can then lead to the baby experiencing difficulty swallowing.

Babies suffering from this condition are often difficult to feed, constantly arching their backs and screaming during and after a feed.

If you think your baby may have a form of reflux you should talk to your GP. Most babies with reflux will have stopped suffering by their first birthday and very few need major intervention by the medical profession.

Things to help a baby suffering from reflux

- Try to keep a reflux baby upright during a feed as gravity helps prevent regurgitation.

- Burp your baby often during a feed.

- Prop one end of the cot up (with phone books, for instance) and put your baby to sleep with her head at the higher end but with her feet still to the bottom of the cot and on her back in the safe sleeping position.

- Try to avoid lifting your baby's legs up while changing her nappy. Roll her onto her side instead.

- If your baby is over eight weeks, do not feed her more than every four hours.

Medications can also help but must be prescribed by a doctor.

Misdiagnosis of reflux

The term 'reflux' is popping up more and more often and seems to be replacing 'colic' as the buzzword used to describe the common scenario of a baby screaming for hours at a time, usually in the evening. First of all, let me say that reflux *does* occur in babies, and in all human beings for that matter. The word itself is defined in the *Oxford English Dictionary* as simply 'backward flow', so in relation to the infant human gastronomic system it generally refers to the backward flow of food from the stomach. Sometimes reflux can be irritating to the oesophagus and baby will communicate this discomfort to parents in the only manner it knows – crying. Genuine reflux can be caused by a number of things, including a dairy allergy or some other form of sensitivity, and should be treated if it persists, but it is my experience that often there is an easier way. Usually, by simply introducing a good routine, you can treat some supposed cases of reflux.

It used to be that doctors and baby health specialists would shrug their shoulders and suggest the baby must have colic when frustrated parents of a restless young sleeper sought medical opinion about their baby's consistent crying. The easy-way-out description of a sleepless baby's condition that colic used to serve as seems to have now been passed to reflux as well as to an obsession with so-called 'dairy allergies'.

When clients say their baby has reflux and won't sleep for any extended period of time, my first reaction is to treat the situation in the same manner as I would colic. I suggest they try my feeding and sleeping solution and the appropriate daily routine as a matter of course before being convinced of the need to treat reflux or allergies. If this doesn't work, then I suggest further consultation with an experienced baby health professional.

As with colic, I believe the cause of reflux is often the way babies are fed and winded. If a baby is not burped completely after each feed, wind builds up in the stomach and creates a bubble that further feeding won't replace. If part of this gaseous bubble gurgles its way out it will often bring liquid contents with it. In such situations, each feed introduces less milk and adds a little more wind to the bubble as the day progresses. Even when you get a good burp or two up after each feed, if it doesn't all come out it will diminish the available room for additional food. By the end of the day, it may only take a minute before your hungry, crying baby can't fit any more food in. The bubble of gas is taking up most of the available stomach space and the screaming starts for two reasons – first, the baby is hungry and second, the build-up of wind is uncomfortable.

Often all the baby needs is a defined and proven feeding and sleeping routine with plenty of attention to burping during and after the bottle or breast (every three minutes if breastfeeding or every 30 ml / 1 oz, if bottle-feeding). Sometimes the burping takes a few minutes, upsetting an already hungry baby further, but most parents agree that a few minutes of crying while winding is better than hours later. Do not continue feeding the baby until you get a burp up or you are sure there is not one left to get up.

Another common cause of consistent crying which may be diagnosed as colic or reflux is the allowance of demand feeding. Feeding your baby every time she cries often leads to the baby having another feed before the previous one has been fully digested. I believe a baby fed too often from the breast can develop reflux because she is getting too much watery foremilk. Once more, the trick here is to have a good routine. Don't give in to the demands and protests; just stick to the scheduled feeding times. About 99 times out of 100, I have found that feeding your baby on a consistent schedule teaches her to take the full amount at each feed. It also gives her sufficient time to digest her feeds completely and eliminate all gas from the stomach. Individual babies take varied amounts of milk or formula at each feed, however it is my experience that they generally thrive on the intervals suggested in my routines.

A baby that is satisfied in its feeding pattern will have far more time and energy to concentrate on its secondary primal instinct in this early stage of life, and that is to sleep soundly as much as possible. Feeding and sleeping are complementary to each other in babies. Irrespective of whether you are told that your baby is suffering from colic or reflux, once you get the feeding routine right, teaching her to settle and resettle herself to sleep will be so much easier.

CONSTIPATION

It is perfectly normal for a breastfed baby to have fewer dirty nappies than a formula-fed baby. This is because breastmilk is often so well digested that there is not too much left to come out as a poo. Some babies over three months go for as long as four days without having a dirty nappy, so you have nothing to worry about if she appears comfortable and her stools are soft when they do appear. A baby is usually only considered constipated if she goes more than seven days without a poo and when it does come it is hard and pellet-shaped. Some formula-fed babies will pass a stool with every feed, and this is also nothing to be concerned about. I often see formula-fed babies who are allowed only a set amount of milk at each feed suffering from constipation – once the amount of milk is increased the constipation goes.

Constipation is rare in babies up to three months, even if formula-fed. Some babies grunt and strain with every movement but this is not necessarily constipation. Still, if your baby cries or looks uncomfortable, check with your health visitor or doctor. If your newborn passes a poo once a day even if it is slightly hard it is not classed as constipation but if your baby passes a hard poo less often than once a day, it is generally considered constipation.

For an older baby who has started solids, symptoms of constipation may include: irritability, abdominal pain and gastric discomfort, a hard abdomen which softens after a bowel movement, blood-streaked stools (usually due to rectal fissures caused by passing hard stools) or hard-to-pass, pellet-like stools.

If your baby does appear constipated, try offering her up to 30 ml (1 oz) of cool, boiled water from a bottle in between the milk feeds. If this is not making any difference, try adding a teaspoon of brown sugar to the water. If (2 oz) is on solids and constipated, try giving her 60 ml (2 oz) of prune juice. If her constipation still doesn't clear up with these home remedies, contact your GP.

I have often found that with babies still solely on milk and those on solids, constipation can be a sign that your baby is hungry, as there is not enough food being given to push though the system. Before trying the remedies above, make sure you are feeding your baby until she is full. If you are breastfeeding make sure you offer both breasts at each feed. If bottle-feeding, ensure you are not feeding a set amount: there should always be some milk left in the bottle at the end of a feed. If your baby drains her bottle you should always make and offer her some more. When feeding solids be sure to offer two courses at each meal time and three times a day once fully established.

There is a very rare condition where a baby suffers from a tight anal sphincter muscle. The baby cries a lot and strains as if constipated with every bowel movement, but when the stool comes it is soft. Not all GPs have come across this condition, so if you think your baby may have it you should ask for a referral to a paediatrician. There is a very simple procedure to correct it.

THRUSH

Thrush is an infection caused by a yeast germ called Candida. Thrush is a very common problem for new mums and babies, especially if one of them has taken antibiotics. In babies thrush is more common in the mouth but is sometimes found to develop in the vagina and around the bottom and it is equally common in boys and girls. If your baby has thrush in her mouth, she will feel sore and uncomfortable and may suddenly be harder to feed. If her mouth appears a brighter red and you can see white spots or a white coating on her tongue she may have thrush.

Some mothers get thrush on their nipples, making them pink and sore, possibly causing shooting pains in the breasts if the thrush has spread to the milk ducts.

Thrush is very easily transmitted between mother and baby and any other family members. It is best if you treat everyone with thrush at the same time to stop repeat infections. If you or your baby has thrush, see your GP to get a suitable treatment. You can carry on breastfeeding while you are being treated for thrush but remember to pay even more attention to hygiene and sterilise everything that comes in contact with your baby's mouth including teats. Try to avoid using dummies while your baby has thrush.

NAPPY RASH

Nappy rash is one of the most common problems GPs see each year. Sometimes the nappy area is infected with thrush or affected by dermatitis, but in most cases the skin under the nappy is damaged by moisture.

Did you know a baby passes very small amounts of urine very frequently, sometimes as often as every fifteen minutes? This means the baby's skin in the nappy area is going to be damp for a large part of the day, which is why you need to take special care of your baby's bottom.

Disposable nappies are generally very good at pulling the moisture away from your baby's skin, but not all nappies are. You should change cloth nappies about twelve times in a 24-hour period and disposable ones about six times in a 24-hour period. Change cloth nappies as often as possible before and after feeds. Always change cloth and disposable nappies after any bowel movement, no matter how small, as the poo can burn the skin. But despite the most intense care, some babies will still get a degree of nappy rash. Putting Sudocrem on at every nappy change will protect the skin from moisture and make it less prone to breaking down.

When washing cloth nappies, try to use pure soap instead of a detergent washing powder, and make sure the nappies are very well rinsed.

If you have tried everything and the nappy rash keeps appearing, see your GP.

COMMON QUESTIONS

Why is my baby's poo green? A baby's first bowel movement is black and tarry (called meconium) and after that her poos will be runny and yellowish. However, breastfed babies have much runnier stools than bottle-fed babies, and the colour depends on what the mother has eaten. Once feeding is established, the colour will settle down. Many parents contact me about green poo but I am yet to find a reason for it! What I can tell you is that green poo comes and goes causing no discernible problems, so if your baby is feeding well and gaining weight, don't worry too much. If her poo is very runny, talk to your GP to rule out an infection. If you find any trace of blood in your baby's poo, you should also contact your GP.

My doctor thinks my baby may have reflux. How can I be sure it's not another problem? You should try your baby on my routine and make sure she is self-settling. If you are on the routine and your baby is sleeping and eating at the correct times but the reflux symptoms are still there, she is most likely suffering from a form of reflux. But if all the symptoms disappear you will know it was not reflux.

My baby keeps falling asleep during a feed – what should I do? This is what I call a sleepy feeder. If she dozes off before taking enough milk to get her to the next feed, you will start to have problems if trying to follow a routine. Try changing her nappy or taking some clothes off as the cool air might rouse her. You could also try putting her down somewhere safe to rest for ten minutes and then try the feed again.

How will I know if my baby has brought up all her wind? The truth is, you won't know. Every baby is slightly different in the amount of winding required, so it is really just a case of trial and error. If your baby is showing signs of an unsettled period in the evening or possetting a lot, try more winding. If she is happy but you feel like you are spending all day winding, try winding her a bit less. If it makes no difference to how content she is then try even less winding. It's all about getting to know your baby.

4

SLEEPING AND SETTLING

How to sleep for long periods by himself is one of the first skills you need to teach your baby. However, one in three children under the age of five does not have this skill and, out of these children, 30 per cent are said to have a serious sleep problem. Did you know that when an adult gets tired she tends to slow down, but when a child or baby gets tired it has the opposite effect and he will speed up and become hyperactive?

Every baby is different in the amount of sleep they need but the table following gives you an idea of what is average; some babies will sleep a lot more and others slightly less.

HOW MUCH SLEEP DOES A BABY NEED?

Age	Total number of hours in a 24-hour period	Total number of hours at night	Total number of hours in the day	Number of daytime sleeps (and naps)
Newborn	15–17	10–11 hours in 2–5 hour blocks	5–6	3–5
Four weeks	15–17	10–11 (broken for feeds)	5–6	3–4

Three months	16 hrs 45 mins	12 (broken for feeds)	4 hrs 45 mins	2 sleeps and 1 nap
Five months	16 hrs 20 mins	12 (broken for feeds with dreamfeed)	4 hrs 20 mins	2 sleeps and 1 nap
Seven months	16	12	4	2
Nine months	15	12	3	2 (or 1 longer sleep and 1 nap)
Twelve months	14 hrs 30 mins	12	2 hrs 30 mins	1 (or 1 longer sleep and 1 nap)
Eighteen months	14 hrs 15 mins	12	2 hrs 15 mins	1
Two years	14	12	2	1
Three years	13	12	1	1 nap

A sleep is when a baby sleeps for more than one sleep cycle (usually longer than 40 minutes), but a nap is one sleep cycle or less.

BEDTIME RITUALS

As I say over and over, babies like to know what is going to happen next and when. One very important habit you can get into from about seven months old is having a bedtime ritual for your baby which will give him clear signals that it is nearly time to go to sleep. Some babies become very upset when put into bed, as though they have been cheated, and I have often thought this is because they were not aware of what was about to happen.

It is very important, however, that you ensure your baby is fully awake when you leave him to go to sleep. If your baby starts to reach that heavy-eyed, falling-asleep stage during your ritual you might be aiding him to sleep, which could lead to him starting to wake through the night. This is because he will have learnt to use the ritual to get to sleep rather than for it to simply indicate bedtime. Therefore, when he wakes during the night he wants that same help to resettle.

If your baby does start waking through the night, you should make changes to your bedtime ritual which will ensure that he is fully awake when you leave their room. For example, you could read two stories on the sofa and just have one short story in bed, or clean his teeth right before sleep time. It is also a good idea to make sure he has his milk drink at least 10–15 minutes before bed.

The bedtime signals may be as big or small as you would like to make them. Some parents start with a story and then say their goodnights to a few favourite toys; others skip the story and just go straight to the goodnights. One little boy I know spends a good ten minutes saying goodnight to each car parked out on his street as his mum shuts the curtains before each sleep; for a younger baby the signal could be as simple as the bath or being swaddled. Whatever it is, the signal should be given at each sleep time before you put your baby down in his cot.

Bathing your baby

For the first week or so, until your baby's umbilical cord stump falls off and the area heals, it's best to stick to a top-to-toe bath with a warm, wet sponge or facecloth. Always wash your baby's face and hands first and his groin last. You should also wash your baby's groin at each nappy change.

After the umbilical cord stump dries up and falls off and the area has healed, you can start giving your baby real baths. While a baby is tiny, it makes most sense to use the kitchen sink or a small plastic baby bath instead of a standard one. Some parents choose to bath their baby every day and make this part of the daily routine, but this is not essential – although once your baby is crawling around you will probably feel you have no choice but to bath or shower him every day! Another option is for your baby to have a shower with you or your partner, but this is really only advisable if there is a second set of hands.

When you do bath your baby, you may find it a little scary at first. Handling a wriggling, wet and soapy little creature takes practise and confidence, so stay calm and maintain a good grip on him. Some babies find the warm water very soothing; if so, let him linger. Others cry through the whole bath or when you get him in and out. Keeping the bathroom warm can help. Another trick is to try putting a wet facecloth on your baby's tummy to help him feel secure while in the bath.

The first bath

- Get everything you need ready first: mild soap, cottonwool balls, towel, nappy and clothes.

- Fill two-thirds of the bath and carefully check the temperature with your elbow. The water should be no hotter than 38°C. A baby can get third-degree burns in less than 50 seconds if the water is at 60°C.

- Making the room warm will help this to be a nice experience for you and your baby and a cold room could give him a shock. Bring your baby to the bath area and undress him completely.

- Gradually slip your baby into the bath feet first, using one hand to support his neck and head. Pour cupfuls of water over him regularly during the bath so he doesn't get too cold.

- To clean him, use just water or a very small amount of mild baby soap as you wash him with your hand or a facecloth from top to bottom, front and back. When your baby is used to having regular baths, a good habit to get into is to wash his face and hair over the bath before you put him in. Use moistened cottonwool balls (no soap) to clean his eyes and face. If dried mucus has collected in the corners of your baby's nostrils or eyes, dab it several times to soften it before you wipe it out. Wash his scalp with a wet, soapy facecloth.

- Rinse your baby thoroughly and then lift him out of the bath, with one hand supporting his neck and head and the other under his bottom, with thumb and forefinger around one thigh. A wet baby can very easily slip out of your hands.

- Wrap your baby in a towel and pat him dry. If his skin tends to be dry, you may want to apply a mild lotion or cream, such as Sudocrem, after his bath. Then put his nappy on and dress him.

> **Tips:**
>
> - Never leave your baby unsupervised, even for a second. If the doorbell or phone rings and you feel you must answer it, wrap him up and take him with you.
>
> - Never put your baby into a bath when the water is still running.

SWADDLING YOUR BABY

It is normal for babies to make jerky movements when they are tired and trying to fall asleep; this is caused by their startle reflex, which is present until they are three to four months old. This is why I always recommend swaddling a baby. I believe swaddled babies settle faster for two reasons. First, babies come from a very confined environment (the womb) with little room for movement and would have felt as though they were being held very tightly. Second, sometimes your baby's jerky movements may wake or frighten him. I don't believe babies realise at first that the hand that keeps appearing is theirs. The only babies I have come across that don't like to be swaddled are overtired babies. I feel it is even more important to swaddle an overtired baby to encourage him to sleep better.

The best-manufactured baby wrap I have found on the market and recommend is the Doublewrap. I have found most babies cannot get out of this wrap. There are many ways to swaddle a baby, and it can be daunting for a new parent to have to learn how to swaddle their new baby. With a Doublewrap, swaddling is made very simple. Everyone putting your baby to bed will swaddle him the same way, making him feel very secure. The other great bonus in the Doublewrap is that you can use it over a safe sleeping bag, as I recommend using from eight weeks until as late as ten months. You can use it in a car seat and your buggy or pram because the Doublewrap works well with a five-point harness (the straps that secure your baby into a car seat or buggy) which makes getting out and about on a routine even easier.

I understand that babies are expensive and not everyone will be able to afford the luxury of a Doublewrap, so as an alternative I recommend swaddling your baby in a 120 cm square of stretch cotton or bamboo fabric. There are many ways to wrap a baby – here's the one I use. Fold one corner down so it is partly in a triangle. Place the baby with his head outside the folded down edge and his feet pointing to the opposite corner (make sure his shoulders are below the folded edge). Put his right arm straight down by his side and bring the left corner of the triangle over the baby, tucking it firmly under his bottom. Put his left arm down by his side and bring the right corner of the triangle over the baby and tuck it under his bottom again.

Swaddling a baby plays an important role in reducing the risk of cot death because it helps to keep your baby in the safe back-sleeping position. I recommend you swaddle your baby until he is at least six months or you notice he is attempting to roll swaddled. Some babies do not attempt to roll swaddled until as late as ten months. Your baby will roll outside bed a lot earlier than this, but you'll only need to remove the swaddle when he shows signs of trying to roll in bed while swaddled.

If you are following my routines your baby will feel safe and secure, so you should not have a problem removing the swaddle. I suggest as soon as you notice your baby is trying to roll swaddled you take the swaddle off him at the next morning sleep. If you follow my comforter advice on page 68, and have your baby in a Save Our Sleep recommended safe sleeping bag, he should get through this transition without any fuss.

However, if your baby is not in a good routine, I would recommend swaddling him until he is four months old, or when he starts to move more during his up time. This will need to be a slow transition. Because your baby will not feel as safe and secure as a baby in a routine, taking the swaddle away all of a sudden could cause problems. If you are going to take the slow approach to weaning your baby off the swaddle, you need to do it well before there is a risk to his safety. If you wait until your baby is older than four months, he might become tangled in or covered by the swaddle.

To wean a baby that is not on my routine off his swaddle start by taking one arm out of the swaddle for three nights, then the second arm out for three nights. Next, just put the swaddle around your baby's waist for three nights and then take it away altogether. When you remove your baby's swaddle I recommend you change the 'tog' (a measure of thermal resistance) of the safe sleeping bag your baby is sleeping in. I recommend you swaddle your baby over a 1 tog safe sleeping bag and when you remove the swaddle to change to a 2.5 tog safe sleeping bag. This means you will not need to adjust the bedding you are using over your safe sleeping bag.

SLEEPING AIDS

The difference between what I call a 'comforter' (see page 68) and a 'sleeping aid' can be confusing at first because in essence, they are both aids to sleep, but they work in significantly different ways. Sleeping aids such as rocking, patting, feeding or giving your baby a dummy to suck on while going to sleep all require your attention and may become a problem for that reason. However, something that provides comfort and which the baby can easily find himself when he wakes in the middle of the night or between sleep cycles can be a parent's best friend.

To dummy or not to dummy?

Giving your baby a dummy has its advantages and disadvantages and it is up to parents to decide which outweighs which in individual cases. What I can do is explain to you when I have recommended *controlled* dummy use to my clients, and why.

I call a dummy a 'stretcher', because I use it to stretch a baby when I am putting him on a new routine. I find this 'controlled dummy use' ideal when moving a baby from one routine to another. There are two other situations in which I have agreed with parents and professionals who have wanted to practise controlled dummy use. One is when premature babies in hospital are given a dummy to help them develop their sucking reflex. The second is when parents of a thumb-sucker prefer to introduce a dummy as they feel it will be easier to wean their baby off the dummy. Thumbs are harder to put in the bin or leave out for Santa.

In my experience, dummies are a common cause of sleep problems. Of the parents who contact me about their baby waking every two hours during the night and catnapping during the day, 60 per cent are giving their child a dummy as a getting-to-sleep aid. Another ten per cent use other sleep aids, such as rocking, patting or feeding. There are seven reasons why a baby with a dummy wakes more frequently than one without.

- A baby with a dummy often finds it harder to achieve a deep sleep as their intermittent sucking will disturb their sleep pattern. Babies need sleep to grow and gain weight and an overtired baby will drink less milk because he associates sucking with falling asleep, so won't suck the bottle or breast in case he starts to fall asleep. Often, babies will suck the breast or bottle until the point of falling asleep and then stop and scream, which is often mistaken for reflux.

- A baby who goes to sleep with a dummy will wake up expecting to suck, but if the dummy has fallen out he will shout for you to come and put it in again. Unfortunately, by the time you go in to replace the dummy, your baby may be so awake that it is hard for him to get back to sleep.

- The constant sucking can trick your baby's body into thinking there is food coming, which causes him to digest the milk feed too fast and makes him hungrier than a baby without a dummy.

- Sucking can be hard work for some babies. When a baby realises he is not getting rewarded for his hard work with food, he may stop linking sucking with the reward of food, and subsequently refuse to suck when offered the breast or bottle.

- Dummy use can also interfere with speech development. If you watch a contented baby lying in his cot, he will be looking around and making babbling sounds. This is the baby's first attempts at speech. A baby with a dummy, however, will be concentrating on sucking and will not be looking around or babbling. Also, take notice of what it says on the label of most dummies, as many manufacturers advise you to never leave your baby unattended with a dummy in case they chew off the top and choke on or swallow it.

- Babies who suck on dummies are at higher risk of ear infections, which may lead to high fevers and the need for antibiotics, both of which have their own side effects.

- A dummy can mask other problems. If a baby is crying and will not settle there is a usually a reason, and a dummy can make this difficult to determine. Often when a baby finishes his feed a parent will pop a dummy in straight away, as the baby is unsettled. Sometimes, the baby is crying because he needs more milk or has wind.

Some research suggests dummy use reduces the risk of cot death, but for me the problems associated with using a dummy outweigh this possible benefit.

In my opinion, the most important thing you can ever teach your baby is how to self-settle, enabling him to drift from one sleep cycle to the next without your help – or the aid of a dummy – to resettle. Discouraging dependency on any aid at bedtime can be difficult initially but I think it is well worthwhile in the end.

Tip: Before giving a crying baby a dummy, make sure nothing is wrong in the first place. A dummy might mask a problem.

Comforter

A comforter is what I class as a 'good' aid, something your baby uses to go to sleep but that he does not need your help with between sleep cycles. Every baby uses an aid of some sort to comfort himself with just before he goes to sleep but unless parents have introduced the aid themselves, they are usually unaware of just what it is (with the exception of thumb-sucking). An unintroduced comforter could be holding, rubbing or playing peekaboo with the sheets or blankets, but sometimes it can be a little more complicated. I have seen babies play with the bars in their cots just before falling asleep which can cause a problem when you ask them to fall asleep in a travel cot or anywhere away from their beloved cot bars. Another common comforter is playing with labels or tags on bedding or clothing.

Luke's story

Up until ten months old, Luke had always been a good sleeper, having been started on my routines at five weeks old. At ten weeks he started to sleep all night and had done so nearly every night since. But suddenly at ten months he was finding it hard to go to sleep and, once asleep, was waking up crying several times throughout the night. I consulted with Luke's parents several times over the phone but we couldn't work out what the problem was, so a house visit was the only option.

After Luke was put to bed, I decided to sneak into his room on all fours and observe him. At first, things appeared okay and Luke was lying down looking ready for sleep. As I watched I noticed a funny movement of his hand. He was putting his fingers down as though trying to scratch his wrist before becoming frustrated and starting to cry. It was not the cry of a baby fighting sleep but of a tearful and genuinely upset baby. I picked him up and went to talk to his parents. After a few minutes we realised he was looking for the sleeves of his winter pyjamas but, as he was now in short sleeves for summer, he couldn't find them anywhere. It was now obvious what Luke's problem had been. We put Luke back in long sleeves and he started sleeping through the night again.

Luke's story was a clear case of a baby who was comforting himself to sleep using an aid that the parents were totally unaware of. It is also a good example of why it is better for parents to choose their baby's comforter for them so they know what it is, but the comforter can be just about anything so long as it is safe with him in his cot.

Choosing a comforter

There are a few things to be aware of when introducing a comforter to your baby:

- Make sure your baby can still breathe if the comforter gets over his face (I suggest cotton muslin squares, or one of the recommended products from the Save Our Sleep website for this reason).

- Make sure your baby cannot get the comforter tangled around his neck (about 35 cm square is a good size for muslin squares).

- Soft toys are not the same as comforters.

- When choosing a comforter, please avoid ones with bean fillings or long fur that your baby might pull out and accidentally inhale. Pull at the fur a little to see how easily it comes away. (Some companies specialise in making baby comforters. They have usually conducted a lot of research into the best comforter features for you and your baby. For safe examples please look in the Save Our Sleep online store.)

- I also recommend that you have more than one comforter, and that they are machine washable. This means you can rotate and wash them periodically as well as ensuring you have a back-up in the event of loss or damage.

Tricks of the trade

There are also a few tricks to introducing a comforter to your baby. Try starting with mum putting it down her top for a few hours (interesting look with a teddy head!) to allow her smell to infiltrate it. Then place the comforter in the cot near baby's face so he can turn and snuggle into it; it is amazing to watch a baby take solace from his comforter.

It is my experience that babies with comforters are much happier and more secure as they progress through certain milestones in their lives. For instance, at about nine months babies often become very clingy to mum when they realise they are individuals and not a part of their mothers; a comforter seems to help with this transition.

Comforters also help babies learn to sleep in different places such as the car, pram and travel cots while on holidays or at day care. And research published recently in Germany suggests that toddlers feel much more secure if they have a comforter with them for the first few visits at kinder or day care. I also support this notion but recommend weaning your child off taking it once he is settled. I also firmly recommend that a comforter is only given to a baby at sleep times or on occasions when some additional comfort is required, such as a visit to hospital or the doctor. In my opinion, it is not good for children or babies to be carrying their comforter around all day. My reason for this is if the comforter is carried around all the time it will no longer help a younger child recognise it as a going-to bed-signal and it will not help the older child with new milestones such as the first day at school because he is used to having it with him all the time.

It is common, at about ten months, for the comforter to start getting thrown out of the cot. The first time it happens could be an accident, so walk in without making eye contact or talking and very calmly return it to the cot. If this becomes a ritual, the baby is probably game-playing. I suggest parents in these situations explain to their baby that if they throw the comforter out it will stay there and he won't have it to sleep with. If the behaviour continues, don't go in straight away but instead wait until you feel your baby has realised his comforter might not be coming back. Then walk in without eye contact or talking and give it back. Each time wait considerably longer and the game will soon stop.

SETTLING YOUR NEW BABY TO SLEEP

One of my most important rules when it comes to babies and their sleep is to always put your baby down to sleep where you intend him to wake up, and to always put him to bed awake. Enabling a baby to settle himself is the key to successful sleep patterns. If you rock, cuddle, feed or give your baby a dummy to go to sleep, then this is what he will expect to have when he comes into the light stage of the sleep cycle. Instead of resettling, your baby will wake himself up looking for you or the sleep aid, and then cry out for you to put his dummy in or rock, pat or feed him back to sleep.

It can be hard to contemplate teaching a new baby to self-settle because the world is such a new and strange place for him. But I believe it is even more unfair to start a habit of helping him to sleep which you are not going to continue. Let's say you find rocking your new baby to sleep an easy option. What happens when he gets too heavy for you to rock? Perhaps you can buy a rocking chair and sit in it while you rock your older baby to sleep, but by the time your baby is twelve months old you could be getting up four or five times a night to rock him back to sleep between sleep cycles. And if this still works for you, what happens if you have a second baby before your first starts to self-settle and your 20-month-old toddler and your four-week-old baby both need rocking at the same time? As you can see, at some point you will have to stop the rocking. But at what age will it be easier for your baby to understand why you have stopped rocking him to sleep? This is why I believe it's best never to start these habits.

There are two ways I recommend you teach a new baby of up to two weeks old to self-settle and the sooner you take on the challenge, the easier it will be on everyone. The first I suggest to clients who I feel are really committed to teaching their new baby to self-settle and prepared for a bit of initial crying! Make sure your baby is well fed, winded and has a clean nappy, then swaddle him and put him down in bed on his back with his comforter beside him. Go into the kitchen, empty the kettle and refill it with cold water, boil it, make yourself a cup of tea, sit down and drink it. If at the end of your cup of tea your baby is still protesting, go and see if there is a problem such as wind or poo. It is important you listen to your baby's cries and if you think it is an emotional cry offer some milk. Most of the time, before you have even boiled the kettle your baby has gone to sleep.

But in reality, most parents find this advice very hard to carry out (and interestingly fathers seem to find it even harder than most mothers to listen to their baby protest). So I give a second option as follows. Make sure your baby is well fed and winded, then wrap him and put him in bed on his back with his comforter beside him. Allow him to shout (cry) for a minimum of two minutes (time it from when he actually starts to cry, as he may stay quiet for a few minutes at first). The longer you can stay out the better for your baby as going in is more for your sake than your baby's, and always time the period of crying as one minute may seem like ten to a parent.

When your baby is crying, try to listen to the cries. The cry of a baby who is fighting sleep has gaps and the tone and pitch will vary. A protesting cry may sound, for example, like this: waaa, pause for a second, wa, pause, waaaaa, pause, wa, pause, waaaaa, pause, waaaaaa, pause, wa, and so on. You should hear the pauses getting longer as your baby starts to fall asleep. If you are able to watch your baby without him seeing, you will see him shut his eyes and nod off before jumping and yelling again, as though he has realised he is falling asleep.

The cry of an emotional or hungry baby is continuous with no pauses and doesn't vary in pitch or tone, for example: waa, waa, waa, waa, waa. This cry I would never ignore. Get the baby up and look for a problem and, if there is no visible problem, I would offer some more milk.

If in this second method you do decide to go in and help your baby to settle, first wait until the minimum two minutes of protesting has passed. Gently rub or pat your baby's tummy keeping him in the safe back-sleeping position which is believed to lower the risk of cot death. Try to avoid eye contact while settling him. If after 22 minutes your baby is not asleep, get him up for a ten-minute break, then start again. This break is for your benefit more than the baby's. Don't give up. You are going to win this encounter. Repeat until your baby is asleep. If during his protests you reach the 22 minutes and you feel like you can continue without a break, keep going or, if you think your baby is about to settle, keep going. Remember as with all my settling advice in this book once you go in to help your baby settle you stay with him until he is asleep.

When your baby finally goes to sleep he may wake again after just one sleep cycle. Don't let this upset you; focus instead on the fact that he went to sleep in the first place. You won the 'going-to-sleep' challenge! Don't expect your baby to resettle until he learns to settle with little or no fuss in the first place. In my experience, after a few days of following my routine for your baby's age and these settling techniques, he will almost certainly stop catnapping and begin having long day sleeps. But remember that the routine is the most important part.

I recommend that if your baby wakes after just one sleep cycle during the day and you know he needs more sleep, get him up. Praise him for going to sleep in the first place and then perhaps go for a walk or a drive to try to encourage him to sleep more in the recommended sleep time until he has learnt to resettle. But at night-time, feed your baby and then put him back in his bed allowing him to settle to sleep, starting first with the two minutes or more of protesting.

CRYING

Using one of my routines means your baby should cry rarely or not at all because he has no reason to. As a baby on one of my routines does not need to cry when he is tired or hungry, this makes parenting easier, as a lot of the guesswork is taken out. However, if your baby does cry, I feel it is very important for you to listen. Babies need to be listened to. It is unfair on a baby to just desperately try to stop him from crying rather than try to interpret his cries. Put yourself in your baby's place. Imagine you are sad and trying to tell a friend how you felt but, because your friend can't stand your tears, she just keeps saying, 'Come on, stop crying, it will be okay. Can I get you a drink? Maybe something to eat will make you feel better?' Think how you would feel. You would stop crying just to please your friend, but you wouldn't feel any better because your problem wouldn't have been shared or solved.

I believe we need to sit back and try to listen to our babies. Let them know it is okay to cry and tell us how they are feeling. We should not be teaching our babies to be quiet and bottle up their feelings, or to eat something to feel better or to solve a problem. This is why I believe my routines help a lot of parents to interpret their baby's cries, because babies only cry for a few reasons in early life so the cause of the crying should be easier to find.

If your baby is crying and you are following one of my routines, you need to ask yourself why he could be crying. Could the cause be:

1 **A wet or dirty nappy?**

2 **Hunger?** If your baby is on the correct routine for his age and a feed is due within twenty minutes of when the crying started

then yes, hunger could be the problem. Try to take your baby's mind off the hunger and wait until the feed time. If all else fails then feed him early, but try to stretch him back slowly onto the routine over the next few feeds. If it is over twenty minutes until the next feed time it could be another problem.

3   **Tired?** If your baby didn't sleep as long as normal at his last sleep or it is within twenty minutes of a scheduled sleep, tiredness could be the problem. I recommend you put him to bed early.

4   **Wind?** If your baby seems stiff and when you lay him down brings both knees up to his tummy, it could be wind. I suggest you sit and wind him. But before the next feed, read my information on colic and wind (chapter 3).

5   **Thirsty?** Your baby could be thirsty. If your baby is four months or older, try giving him a drink of water. This is a good habit to get into because water is very good for everyone. But as mentioned previously, never give a younger baby more than 30 ml (1 oz) between milk feeds. If your baby is bored, a drink of water might also entertain him and help him feel a bit better.

6   **Hot or cold?** Could your baby be hot or cold? The best guide is usually to dress babies in layers and put one extra layer on than you are wearing.

7   **Bored?** If your baby is not due for a feed or sleep, he could be bored. Try reading him a book or showing him a toy. Maybe he might just feel like a cuddle. Or, he might be in an uncomfortable position and moving him might help.

If you have covered all of the above, then your baby may have a different problem, maybe a pain brought on by food intolerance. You should talk to your doctor if the crying continues.

If the crying won't stop

A crying baby can really try your patience. If you have tried everything and you just can't get your baby to stop crying, you will probably start to feel quite tense and upset. This is understandable but will not help the situation. Your baby will pick up on your feelings and cry even more. There is no doubt that tender, loving care and sympathy from a calm, caring adult will reassure and help your baby at least to some extent. But if you are upset yourself, you may not be able to provide this comfort. If you are tense, or at the point where you can't take any more, this is a danger signal and you shouldn't ignore these feelings. You may need to put your baby down in a safe place like his cot and go and recharge your own batteries. Try making yourself a cup of tea and phoning a friend for a chat or taking a shower. You may even be pleasantly surprised to find he falls asleep while you are having the break.

If you are at the point where you can't even get out of bed to go and look after your baby, you need to ask for help. A lot of parents and carers find it all gets too much, but this problem won't go away. Call anyone who will listen and take your problem seriously – your GP, health vistor, or even the Samaritans. If you are trying to call a help line and seem to be queuing for hours, this may make you even more upset so hang up and try calling someone else.

Crying while changing sleep habits

If you have not followed my routines from the beginning of your child's life and sleep problems have started, then there will be some protesting (crying) until the problems are resolved. It is important to remember that a protesting cry is inevitable when teaching a baby to settle himself and doesn't necessarily mean that something is seriously wrong. Be reassured that this crying will become less frequent and shorter in duration as the baby develops self-settling skills. The challenge for parents is to resist the temptation to comfort their baby every time he protests.

The main thing parents of older babies need to understand is the differences between a protest cry, which is like a temper tantrum, and an emotional cry, which occurs because a baby's needs are not being met. If a baby is crying an emotional cry, you will see tears and hear sobbing (I often call this a wet cry). You should comfort an emotional baby straight away. I feel very strongly that ignoring an emotional cry could cause psychological damage and stress to a baby, which is why I disagree with controlled crying, as walking in and then out is like teasing the baby and always makes him emotional. With controlled crying, after a baby falls asleep he will continue to sob – this is what I call crying yourself to sleep. The other problem with controlled crying is that it can go on for hours at a time and sometimes take weeks before you see any results.

However, if you are using one of my approaches, your baby will most likely be crying a protesting cry without the tears and sobbing. I believe you can ignore this protest for as long as it takes for your baby to go to sleep. The noticeable difference is that he will stop protesting and go to sleep from a calm state, without any tears or sobbing before or after falling asleep. A baby who is protesting, as with a toddler having a temper tantrum, will not protest for long.

I have often read that babies don't produce tears until as late as six months but I doubt the truth of this and have seen babies as young as six weeks crying with tears and emotion. Perhaps the belief came about because most babies have no reason to cry an emotional cry until six months.

Controlled crying from the baby's point of view

One of the reasons I am against controlled crying is because I look at it from the baby's perspective. Depending on whose version of controlled crying you use, you are told to put your baby in his bed and allow him to cry for a certain amount of time. After that time, if still crying, you return and talk to or touch your baby for a few seconds to a minute and then you leave again. Usually the length of time you stay out increases each time you leave your baby.

From your baby's point of view, this behaviour just sends confusing mixed messages. When you put him in his cot he may start a protesting cry as you say goodnight and walk out of the room. At this point he will be yelling something along the lines of, 'I don't want to go to sleep! Don't leave me in this cot – get back in here and pick me up.' I don't believe this protesting cry will harm your baby in any way. In my settling guidelines, if you go back in to your baby after this point, you stay in the room with him until he is asleep, so your baby never gets to the emotional crying stage.

But in controlled crying, when you return to the room your baby thinks he will be picked up. When this doesn't happen and instead you comfort briefly then turn and walk back out, he will become emotional and upset. This is the point when baby feels betrayed and heartbroken and why I equate it to teasing your baby. To make the whole thing worse, you then keep coming in at different intervals and walking out again. How confusing this must be! Eventually the baby is so exhausted he falls asleep, but sometimes he gets so hot from the emotional crying he even vomits. The other problem is that you are really just teaching him to cry for longer amounts of time and then you will come back in.

Over the years I have met parents who claim controlled crying has worked for them, but usually when I question further I find out it has either taken weeks (which says to me the baby has just given up crying, feeling there is no point because his cries have been ignored) or the parents have worked out for themselves that their baby gets too upset if they go in and out, so they have started doing something more like my approach anyway.

THE SOCIETY WE LIVE IN

I believe the way we live today is a big factor in why we are now seeing so many sleep and other problems in babies. In years gone by, larger families who lived much closer together meant mothers, aunts or other experienced relatives visited frequently, perhaps even daily, and new mothers were handed down lots of tips and little bits of advice. These days with older generations living further away or working full-time, these visits are much fewer. I think grandparents try to give the same advice at times but, because they are around a lot less, they give too much advice at once and this is often seen as interfering. Some young parents shut their ears and don't take the advice in; others try to but can't take in so much information at once.

Larger families also meant young girls learnt the skill of mothering very early, not by choice but because their role in the family was to help with the babies and younger children while mothers spent most of the day keeping the household running. For better or for worse, today's society is very different. In fact, leaving your six-year-old to mind the baby could find you in trouble with the law! In today's society, because we no longer have our extended family close by, I feel it is very important you go to your local baby clinic and join the mothers' group for your baby's age. When you first have your baby the idea of going once a week or fortnight to this group often feels like a big chore. But believe me you will be pleased you made the effort because you will be able to ask the nurse lots of questions; and the mothers and babies you meet now, you will most likely stay friends with and use as a support network until your baby starts school.

COMMON QUESTIONS

Is it normal for my baby to wake in the night but not need any attention? Yes, it is. We all sleep in sleep cycles, starting with a shallow cycle followed by a deep cycle, and we all wake in the night between these cycles. As adults we just turn, get comfortable, then go back to sleep, but it can often take young children and babies a few minutes to get back to sleep. Research shows that the more a parent tries to help a child get from one sleep cycle to the next, the less likely it is that the child will sleep through the night. Therefore, the less interference the better.

Is it really all right to let my baby cry? I do not think it is all right to let a baby cry an emotional cry; however, I believe you may let a baby protest (the broken cry you hear when a baby is trying to go to sleep). If you responded every time your baby protested, he would soon learn to protest whenever he wanted your attention. In fact, you would cause him to protest more. It's not fair on a baby to be taught that someone will respond to every protest because, as your baby grows up, other people won't like this behaviour.

I have just moved to a new area and as it is too far to travel to my old mothers' group, how can I join a local one? The best way to find out about your local mothers' group is to call your health centre. Explain to them you are new to the area and they will give you the numbers of some other mothers who had babies at the same time as you. Or they will call the mothers for you and find out if they still meet.

When I settle my baby and he is asleep on his side is it safe to leave him on his side? If I try and roll him back onto his back, he wakes up. No, it is not safe to leave your baby on his side as he may roll onto his tummy and be at risk of cot death. If you find moving him back onto his back wakes him then try rubbing or patting his tummy until he is asleep so you don't have to move him once he is asleep.

5

ROUTINES FROM BIRTH TO INTRODUCING SOLIDS

Both babies and their parents gain from following my routines. The babies benefit because they don't need to cry as much as babies not on a routine (crying being a baby's main method of communication) and they also feel very safe and secure on a routine. Parents benefit from my routines because they find it easier to interpret their baby's cries and can plan their days around sleep and feed times.

The way I developed my routines was from watching babies. I didn't just decide what I thought babies should be doing at certain ages – I watched babies and saw what they did naturally when left to find their own routine. The feedback I often get from parents following my routines is that when their baby's sleep and feeding habits start to change, they go to the next routine stage and find their baby has got there already. This is because my routines are based on the natural feeding and sleeping times for babies.

GROWTH SPURTS WHILE FOLLOWING MY ROUTINES

When I talk about a growth spurt I am talking about a time when your baby will seem hungrier than she usually is. Although we cannot predict when a growth spurt will take place, I have observed times where a baby is more likely to have one, and have therefore allowed for this in my routines. If your baby is bottle-fed, and you are following my advice and feeding her until she is full, you will not need to worry about her growth spurts because she will just drink the extra milk she needs. However, if your baby is breastfed I can't state strongly enough how important it is for a breastfeeding mother to follow the expressing times stated if you want to have your baby both on my routines and breastfeeding successfully. The expressed milk should be kept and given at the 6 pm feed or stored appropriately for a later date.

If you look carefully at my breastfeeding routines you will see that more milk is expressed the week before a common growth spurt than in the weeks your baby may be having a growth spurt. This means there is more milk in your breasts during the week she is having a growth spurt because your breasts have become accustomed to making more milk. Your baby will drink this extra milk during the growth spurt. If you can't express or you choose not to express, you can use my routines only as guides until week eight. At week eight you can follow my routines to the minute because expressing is not required to make the routine work successfully.

If your baby goes through a growth spurt at other times apart from the weeks I have suggested, don't worry. If you have been following my routines and expressing advice, because your breasts will think you have a bigger, hungrier baby, they will produce more than is needed and will be used to making different amounts of milk.

There are a number of reasons you should express before a feed until your baby is eight weeks old.

- Your baby should still be asleep when you are expressing so you can relax and not worry about needing to tend to her. If you try to express after a feed you might need to wind your baby or you might miss out on cuddling time while expressing. Your baby might also fall asleep outside feed time while you express; however, if you are not expressing you can stimulate your baby to keep her awake.

- If you express after a feed you might be expressing after the hour mark which will affect the amount of time your breasts have to make more milk.

- Once your breasts are on a routine for a while, your milk becomes all hind milk. But before this happens, if you express before you feed, you will be expressing fore milk, which is not as important for your baby to drink and in some cases can give her reflux. If you express after the feed you will be taking the hind milk, and this milk is important for your baby.

Once your baby is eight weeks and over then you can follow the advice on pages 107–108. You can begin to express after the 7 am and 11 am feeds, making sure to finish by 8 am and 12 pm respectively.

GETTING OUT AND ABOUT ON A ROUTINE

It is very important that you still get out and about while following a routine. When the routine suggests putting your baby down for a sleep in her cot, it is fine to put her in the pram instead and go out for a walk. When you are a new parent it is very important you don't stay home all day and feel isolated.

Some of my parents make it a habit each day to put their baby in the pram for the 9 am or 1 pm sleep and go for a walk. They walk to a café for breakfast or lunch and then walk home again for the 11 am or 3 pm feed. When the baby gets older they may walk earlier and give her a solid meal at the café. From my experience, the more fresh air and daylight babies get the better they seem to sleep at night.

Tip: When getting out and about on a routine, it is important to use the same bedding and dress your baby the same way she sleeps at home. The Doublewrap and safe sleeping bag should still be used for sleeps in the car seat, buggy or pram. You will need to adjust the amount of blankets you use depending on the outside temperature.

While out and about you can either swaddle your baby and then put the harness on over the top of the Doublewrap. Or you can lay the Doublewrap out and thread it in under the arm section of the five-point harness, then pop your baby in and fold the swaddle over the top of the fastened seat belt. Personally, I prefer to swaddle first and then secure the harness over the top of the wrapped baby, ensuring it is secure over the shoulders.

THE DREAMFEED

Parents I visit are often totally frustrated by having to feed their baby twice or more a night. Just last month I visited Sarah, mum to ten-week-old Tom. She was following a four-hourly feeding routine during the day, putting Tom to bed each night by 7 pm and waking him each morning at 7 am. However, Sarah explained that she felt exhausted as Tom was waking each night at around midnight and then again at 4 am for a feed. She said it felt like each time she just got to sleep then Tom woke again or she had to wake him to start the day.

Sarah had been told she should nap while Tom had his day sleeps. However, with two other children to look after, this was impossible. So I explained to Sarah that in order to encourage Tom to sleep longer at night, we should introduce a dreamfeed. We put Tom onto my routine and introduced a dreamfeed. Within days, Sarah was feeling so much better as Tom was now only waking once a night at 3:30 am. To Sarah's surprise after twelve days of introducing the dreamfeed, Tom was making it through to 7 am without a feed.

The reason I recommend the dreamfeed, is to help parents like Sarah avoid having to get up more than once at night to feed their babies. I normally introduce the dreamfeed when babies are about six weeks old. If you followed my routine but didn't have the dreamfeed, your baby would go to sleep at 7 pm but wake for feeds at around midnight and 4 am like Tom. With the dreamfeed, your baby will wake for her first feed at around 2.30 am and then she is more likely to sleep until 7 am. This means you have only had to get up once at night. As your baby gets older she will wake later and later for this feed until she is sleeping through every night until 7 am.

How to Dreamfeed

To do the 'dreamfeed', gently pick up your sleeping baby, place the bottle or breast on her lower lip and allow her to drink, taking care not to wake her. When finished, sit her upright for a few minutes to allow wind to escape. Babies are usually so relaxed at this feed that they don't gulp air and so don't have much wind. Your baby will not choke during the dreamfeed if you are holding her in your normal feeding position. Babies often sleep while feeding at the breast or from a bottle. Do not try and leave your baby in her bed while you do the dreamfeed.

The dreamfeed is a good feed to get your partner to give your baby from a bottle. If you are breastfeeding this would be a good time to give your baby a bottle of expressed milk. The best time to express is just before the 7 am and 11 am feeds as this is when your breasts are at their fullest.

THE NIGHT FEED

Night feeds are feeds your baby should wake up and demand at night. If your baby has regained her birth weight and is over 3 kg (6.6 lb), you can wait for her to demand these feeds but if she is under 3 kg (6.6 lb) or has not regained her birth weight, you will need to wake her up at night to feed. Some babies are too weak and small to demand a night feed. During night feeds, try not to talk to your baby and keep the lights dim, so she starts to understand the difference between night and day.

BABIES OVER ONE MONTH

If your baby is breastfed and is over one month and under three months when you are reading this book for the first time, I recommend you start my routines with the week four routine rather than your baby's age. Follow each routine for two weeks until you reach the ten-week routine, then your next move of routine will be when you start your baby on solids.

CATNAPPING IN THE FIRST TEN WEEKS

Catnapping in the first ten weeks can be caused by two things. The most common is you are putting your baby to bed when she is tired enough to nap but not tired enough to sleep. If she is catnapping I suggest you try the next routine which will give your little one a bit more awake time. The second reason for catnapping in the age group is hunger. If changing to the next routine doesn't work you will need to rule out hunger as a problem.

ROUTINES FOR BREASTFED BABIES FROM ONE TO EIGHT WEEKS OLD

Routine for a breastfed baby aged one to two weeks

This routine is for a baby aged seven to thirteen days old (and until she regains her birth weight and is over 3 kg / 6.6 lb).

Feed times	Sleep times	Bedtime
7 am	8.15 am	7 pm
10 am	11.30 am	
1 pm	2.30 pm	
4 pm		
6 pm		
9.30 pm		
2.30 am (at the latest)		

6.40 am

Express as much as you can, up to 90 ml (3 oz), from your *right* breast.

7 am

Wake your baby up and feed her for up to 25 minutes from your *left* breast. You will wake and feed her even if she last fed at 5.30 am, so she is always starting her day at the same time and on a full tummy. Then feed her for up to fifteen minutes from your *right* breast.

8.15 am

Swaddle your baby and put her in bed on her back awake and allow her to self-settle (see guide to self-settling starting on page 187).

9.40 am

Express as much as you can, up to 90 ml (3 oz), from your *left* breast.

10 am

Wake your baby up and feed her for up to 25 minutes from your *right* breast. Then feed her for up to fifteen minutes from your *left* breast.

11.30 am
Swaddle your baby and put her in bed on her back awake and allow her to self-settle.

1 pm
Wake your baby up and feed her for up to 25 minutes from your *left* breast. Then feed her for up to 25 minutes from your *right* breast.

2.30 pm
Swaddle your baby and put her down in bed on her back awake and allow her to self-settle.

4 pm
Wake your baby up and feed her for up to 25 minutes from your *right* breast. Then feed her for up to 25 minutes from your *left* breast. After this feed, put your baby down somewhere comfortable and safe, so if she feels like having a little nap before her bath she may. But don't put her in bed as she may choose not to sleep.

5.20 pm
Bath baby, or give top-to-toe wash.

6 pm
Feed your baby for up to 25 minutes from your *left* breast. Then feed her for up to 25 minutes from your *right* breast. Or you or another carer could give her a bottle of expressed milk. If you don't breastfeed your baby at the 6 pm feed during the first week of the routine while establishing breastfeeding, you should express 30 ml (1 oz) from each breast at 8 pm instead of the suggested time of 9 pm.

7 pm
Swaddle your baby and put her in bed on her back awake and allow her to self-settle.

9 pm

Express as much as you can, up to 90 ml (3 oz), from your *right* breast.

9.30 pm

Wake your baby up and feed her for up to 25 minutes from your *left* breast. Then feed her for up to fifteen minutes from your *right* breast.

Night feeds

Set your alarm clock for 2.30 am every night: in case your baby has not woken for a feed it is very important you don't go more than five hours without feeding her on this routine. But if your baby woke, for example, at 12.30 am, then reset your alarm clock for 5.30 am. If she woke any time after 1.35 am and fed, however, reset your alarm for just before 6.40 am, so you can get up and express. If your baby wakes at 6.30 am, or while you are expressing, and is crying you should feed her. If your baby seems content to wait then you should try to express first and feed her as near to 7 am as possible. However, if you feed her first you should express after the feed. During night feeds, try not to talk to your baby and keep the lights dim so she starts to understand the difference between night and day.

Important note: By two weeks old your baby should be back to her original birth weight. If she has regained her birth weight and is over 3 kg (6.6 lb), you may advance to the two-to four-week routine. If your baby has not regained her birth weight or is still under 3 kg (6.6 lb), please stay on the above routine until she has reached these goals. When you do advance to the next routine, follow each routine for two weeks until you reach the ten-week routine. Then your next move of routine will be when your baby starts on solids.

> **Tip:** If you find your baby is too sleepy after a bath to take a good feed try feeding her on one breast before the bath and the other side after the bath.

Routine for a breastfed baby aged two to four weeks

This routine is for a baby aged fourteen to 27 days old who has regained her birth weight and is over 3 kg (6.6 lb).

Feed times	Sleep times	Bedtime
7 am	8.15 am	7 pm
10 am	11.30 am	
1 pm	2.30 pm	
4 pm		
6 pm		
9.30 pm		
3.30 am (at the latest)		

6.40 am
Express as much as you can, up to 30 ml (1 oz), from your *right* breast.

7 am
Wake your baby up and feed her for up to 25 minutes from your *left* breast. You will wake and feed her even if she last fed at 5.30 am, so she is always starting her day at the same time and on a full tummy. Then feed her for up to fifteen minutes from your *right* breast.

8.15 am
Swaddle your baby and put her in bed on her back awake and allow her to self-settle (see guide to self-settling starting on page 187).

9.40 am
Express as much as you can, up to 60 ml (2 oz) from your *left* breast.

10 am
Wake your baby up and feed her for up to 25 minutes from your *right* breast. Then feed her for fifteen minutes from your *left* breast.

11.30 am
Swaddle your baby and put her in bed on her back awake and allow her to self-settle.

1 pm
Wake your baby up and feed her for up to 25 minutes from your *left* breast. Then feed her for up to 25 minutes from your *right* breast.

2.30 pm
Swaddle your baby and put her in bed on her back awake and allow her to self-settle.

4 pm
Wake your baby up and feed her for up to 25 minutes from your *right* breast. Then feed her for up to 25 minutes from your *left* breast. After this feed, put your baby down somewhere comfortable and safe, so if she feels like having a little nap before her bath she may. But don't put her in bed as she may choose not to sleep.

5.20 pm
Bath baby, or give top-to-toe wash.

6 pm
Feed your baby for up to 25 minutes from your *left* breast. Then feed her for up to 25 minutes from your *right* breast. Or you or another carer could give her a bottle of expressed milk. If you don't breastfeed your baby at the 6 pm feed during the second week of the routine while establishing breastfeeding, you should express 30 ml (1 oz) from each breast at 8 pm instead of the suggested time of 9.10 pm. Aim for this feed to end at 6.50 pm, so if you find your baby usually only takes 30 minutes to take her full feed, including winding, start this feed at 6.20 pm.

7 pm
Swaddle your baby and put her in bed on her back awake and allow her to self-settle.

9.10 pm
Express as much as you can, up to 90 ml (3 oz), from your *right* breast.

9.30 pm
Wake your baby up and feed her for up to 25 minutes from your *left* breast. Then feed her for up to fifteen minutes from your *right* breast.

Night feeds
Now you are in the third week and your baby has regained her birth weight and is over 3 kg (6.6 lb), you may let her sleep a bit longer at night, but don't go more than six hours without expressing or feeding your baby. If you choose to express rather than waking and feeding your baby, you only need to express 30 ml (1 oz) from each breast to keep your supply up. Set your alarm clock for 3.30 am each night to do this. If your baby wakes and feeds any time before 12.40 am then you will need to recalculate and reset your alarm clock for six hours after that feed begins. However, if she wakes at 12.40 am or later, reset your alarm for just before 6.40 am so you can get up and express. During night feeds, try not to talk to your baby and keep the lights dim so she starts to understand the difference between night and day.

Growth spurt note: A baby normally goes through a growth spurt at about three weeks which has been allowed for in the above routine.

Routine for a breastfed baby aged four to six weeks

This routine is for a baby aged 28 to 41 days old.

Feed times	Sleep times	Bedtime
7 am	8.15 am	7 pm
10.15 am	11.45 am	
1.30 pm	3 pm	
4.45 pm		**Dreamfeed**
6 pm		9.45 pm

6.40 am
Express as much as you can, up to 90 ml (3 oz), from your *right* breast.

7 am
Wake your baby up and feed her for up to 25 minutes from your *left* breast. You will wake and feed her even if she last fed at 5.30 am, so she is always starting her day at the same time and on a full tummy. Then feed her for up to fifteen minutes from your *right* breast.

8.15 am
Swaddle your baby and put her in bed on her back awake and allow her to self-settle (see the guide to self-settling starting on page 187).

9.40 am
Express as much as you can, up to 90 ml (3 oz), from your *left* breast.

10.15 am
Wake your baby up and feed her for up to 25 minutes from your *right* breast. Then feed her for up to fifteen minutes from your *left* breast.

11.45 am
Swaddle your baby and put her in bed on her back awake and allow her to self-settle.

1.30 pm
Wake your baby up and feed her for up to 25 minutes from your *left* breast. Then feed her for up to 25 minutes from your *right* breast.

3 pm
Swaddle your baby and put her in bed on her back awake and allow her to self-settle.

4.45 pm
Wake your baby up and feed her for up to 25 minutes from your *right* breast. Then feed her for up to 25 minutes from your *left* breast. After this feed, put your baby down somewhere comfortable and safe, so if she feels like having a little nap before her bath she may. But don't put her in bed as she may choose not to sleep.

5.45 pm
Bath baby, or give top-to-toe wash.

6 pm
Feed your baby for up to 25 minutes from your *left* breast. Then feed her for up to 25 minutes from your *right* breast. Or you or another carer could give her a bottle of expressed milk (please note you don't need to change expressing time because the lengths of time your breasts are left without stimulating are fine on this routine). Aim for this feed to end at 6.50 pm, so if you find your baby usually only takes 30 minutes to take her full feed, including winding, start this feed at 6.20 pm.

7 pm
Swaddle your baby and put her in bed on her back awake and allow her to self-settle.

9.25 pm
Express as much as you can, up to 90 ml (3 oz), from your *right* breast.

9.45 pm
Give your baby a dreamfeed, starting the feed from your *left* breast.

Night feeds
Feed your baby when she wakes during the night. During night feeds, try not to talk to her and keep the lights dim so she starts to understand the difference between night and day.

Tip: If your baby sleeps all night and wakes at 6.15 am for the first time I suggest getting her up and feeding her straight away then as soon as the feed is over pop her back to bed. Please let her sleep twenty minutes or until 7 am, which ever is later, offering her a top-up feed at this time. Please keep her up until the time of her next routine sleep.

Routine for a breastfed baby aged six to eight weeks

This routine is for a baby aged 42 to 55 days old.

Feed times	Sleep times	Bedtime
7 am	8.30 am	7 pm
11 am	12.30 pm	
2.45 pm	**Nap**	**Dreamfeed**
6 pm	4.15 pm	10 pm

6.40 am

Express as much as you can, up to 30 ml (1 oz), from your *right* breast.

7 am

Wake your baby up and feed her for up to 25 minutes from your *left* breast. You will wake and feed her even if she last fed at 5.30 am, so she is always starting her day at the same time and on a full tummy. Then feed her for up to 25 minutes from your *right* breast.

8.30 am

Swaddle your baby and put her in bed on her back awake and allow her to self-settle (see guide to self-settling starting on page 187).

11 am

Wake your baby up and feed her for up to 25 minutes from your *right* breast. Then feed her for up to 25 minutes from your *left* breast.

12.30 pm

Swaddle your baby and put her in bed on her back awake and allow her to self-settle.

2.45 pm

Wake your baby up and feed her for up to 25 minutes from your *left* breast. Then feed her for up to 25 minutes from your *right* breast.

4.15 pm
Take your baby for a walk or out in the car to encourage her to sleep in places other than her bed.

5.15 pm
Wake your baby up if necessary. Sleeping past 5.15 pm could affect how well your baby settles at 7 pm.

5.40 pm
Bath baby, or give top-to-toe wash.

6 pm
Feed your baby for up to 25 minutes from your *right* breast. Then feed her for up to 25 minutes from your *left* breast. Or you or another carer could give her a bottle of expressed milk. If you don't breastfeed your baby at this feed, you should express 90 ml (3 oz) from each breast at 7.30 pm rather than the suggested time of 9.40 pm. Aim for this feed to end at 6.50 pm, so if you find your baby usually only takes 30 minutes to take her full feed, including winding, start this feed at 6.20 pm.

7 pm
Swaddle your baby and put her in bed on her back awake and allow her to self-settle.

9.40 pm
Express as much as you can, up to 90 ml (3 oz), from your *left* breast.

10 pm
Give your baby a dreamfeed, starting from your *right* breast.

Night feeds
Feed your baby when she wakes during the night. During night feeds, try not to talk to her and keep the lights dim so she starts to understand the difference between night and day.

Growth spurt note: A baby normally goes through a growth spurt at about six weeks which has been allowed for in the above routine.

ROUTINES FOR BOTTLE-FED BABIES FROM NEWBORN TO EIGHT WEEKS OLD

Routine for a bottle-fed baby aged newborn to two weeks

This routine is for a baby aged one to thirteen days old (and until she regains her birth weight and is over 3 kg / 6.6 lb).

Feed times	Sleep times	Bedtime
7 am	8.15 am	7 pm
10.30 am	11.45 am	
2 pm	3.15 pm	
6 pm		
9.30 pm		
3.30 am (at the latest)		

Important note: Always feed your baby until she is full – never give your baby a set amount.

7 am
Wake your baby up and feed her a bottle. You will wake and feed her even if she last fed at 5.30 am, so she is always starting her day at the same time and on a full tummy.

8.15 am
Swaddle your baby and put her in bed on her back awake and allow her to self-settle (see guide to self-settling starting on page 187).

10.30 am
Wake your baby up and feed her a bottle.

11.45 am
Swaddle your baby and put her in bed on her back awake and allow her to self-settle.

2 pm

Wake your baby up and feed her a bottle.

3.15 pm

Swaddle your baby and put her in bed on her back awake and allow her to self-settle.

5.30 pm

Wake your baby up and bath her, or give top-to-toe wash.

6 pm

Feed your baby a bottle.

7 pm

Swaddle your baby and put her in bed on her back awake and allow her to self-settle.

9.30 pm

Wake your baby up and feed her a bottle.

Night feeds

Until your baby has regained her birth weight, and is over 3 kg (6.6 lb), she should not be allowed to sleep longer than six hours at night without a feed. Set your alarm for 3.30 am every night. But if your baby woke, for example, at 11.30 pm and fed, then reset your alarm clock for 5.30 am. If she woke any time after 1 am and fed, however, reset your alarm for just before 7 am so you can get up and start her day. During night feeds, try not to talk to your baby and keep the lights dim so she starts to understand the difference between night and day. If your baby has regained her birth weight and is also over 3 kg (6.6 lb), you may allow her to sleep at night until she wakes looking for a feed.

Important note: By two weeks old your baby should be back to her original birth weight. If your baby has regained her birth weight and is over 3 kg (6.6 lb), you may advance to the two- to four-week routine. If your baby has not regained her birth weight or is still under 3 kg (6.6 lb), please stay on the above routine until she has reached these goals. When you do advance to the next routine, follow each routine for two weeks until you reach the ten-week routine. Then your next move of routine will be when your baby starts on solids.

Tip: If you find your baby is too sleepy after a bath to take a good feed, try giving her half her feed before the bath and the other half after the bath.

Routine for a bottle-fed baby aged two to four weeks

This routine is for a baby aged fourteen to 27 days old who has regained her birth weight and is over 3 kg (6.6 lb).

Feed times	Sleep times	Bedtime
7 am	8.15 am	7 pm
11 am	12.30 pm	
3 pm	4.30 pm	
6 pm		
10 pm		

7 am
Wake your baby up and feed her a bottle. You will wake and feed her even if she last fed at 5.30 am, so she is always starting her day at the same time and on a full tummy.

8.15 am
Swaddle your baby and put her in bed on her back awake and allow her to self-settle (see guide to self-settling starting on page 187).

11 am
Wake your baby up and feed her a bottle.

12.30 pm
Swaddle your baby and put her in bed on her back awake and allow her to self-settle.

3 pm
Wake your baby up and feed her a bottle.

4.30 pm
Swaddle your baby and put her in bed on her back awake and allow her to self-settle.

5.30 pm
Wake your baby up and bath her, or give top-to-toe wash.

6 pm
Feed your baby a bottle.

7 pm
Swaddle your baby and put her in bed on her back awake and allow her to self-settle.

10 pm
Wake your baby up and feed her a bottle.

Night feeds
Feed your baby when she wakes during the night. During night feeds, try not to talk to her and keep the lights dim so she starts to understand the difference between night and day.

Routine for a bottle-fed baby aged four to six weeks

This routine is for a baby aged 28 to 41 days old.

Feed times	Sleep times	Bedtime
7 am	8.15 am	7 pm
11 am	12.30 pm	
3 pm	**Nap**	**Dreamfeed**
6 pm	4.30 pm	10 pm

7 am
Wake your baby up and feed her a bottle. You will wake and feed her even if she last fed at 5.30 am, so she is always starting her day at the same time and on a full tummy.

8.15 am
Swaddle your baby and put her in bed on her back awake and allow her to self-settle (see guide to self-settling starting on page 187).

11 am
Wake your baby up and feed her a bottle.

12.30 pm
Swaddle your baby and put her in bed on her back awake and allow her to self-settle.

3 pm
Wake your baby up and feed her a bottle.

4.30 pm
Take your baby for a walk or out in the car to encourage her to sleep in places other than her bed.

5.30 pm
Wake your baby up and bath her, or give top-to-toe wash.

6 pm
Feed your baby a bottle.

7 pm
Swaddle your baby and put her in bed on her back awake and allow her to self-settle.

10 pm
Give your baby a dreamfeed.

Night feeds
Feed your baby when she wakes during the night. During night feeds, try not to talk to her and keep the lights dim so she starts to understand the difference between night and day.

Tip: If your baby sleeps all night and wakes at 6.15 am for the first time I suggest getting her up and feeding her straight away then as soon as the feed is over pop her back to bed. Please let her sleep twenty minutes or until 7 am, which ever is later, offering her a top-up feed at this time. Please keep her up until the time of her next routine sleep.

Routine for a bottle-fed baby aged six to eight weeks

This routine is for a baby aged 42 to 55 days old.

Feed times	Sleep times	Bedtime
7 am	8.30 am	7 pm
11 am	12.30 pm	
3 pm	**Nap**	**Dreamfeed**
6.20 pm	4.30 pm	10 pm

7 am

Wake your baby up and feed her a bottle. You will wake and feed her even if she last fed at 5.30 am, so she is always starting her day at the same time and on a full tummy.

8.30 am

Swaddle your baby and put her in bed on her back awake and allow her to self-settle (see guide to self-settling starting on page 187).

11 am

Wake your baby up and feed her a bottle.

12.30 pm

Swaddle your baby and put her in bed on her back awake and allow her to self-settle.

3 pm

Wake your baby up and feed her a bottle.

4.30 pm

Take your baby for a walk or out in the car to encourage her to sleep in places other than her bed.

5.30 pm

Wake your baby up and bath her, or give top-to-toe wash.

6.20 pm
Feed your baby a bottle.

7 pm
Swaddle your baby and put her in bed on her back awake and allow her to self-settle.

10 pm
Give your baby a dreamfeed.

Night feeds
Feed your baby when she wakes during the night. During night feeds, try not to talk to her and keep the lights dim so she starts to understand the difference between night and day.

Tip: From the time your baby is on my eight- to ten-week routine you will no longer need to express milk to use my routines. However, if you want to continue to give your baby a bottle of expressed milk once a day you will need to express. This expressing should be done at the same time every day after either the 7 am or 11 am feeds or both depending on how much you need and how much you are able to express.

ROUTINES FOR BOTH BREASTFED AND BOTTLE-FED BABIES FROM EIGHT WEEKS OLD

Routine for a baby aged eight to ten weeks

This routine is for a baby aged 56 to 69 days old.

Feed times	Sleep times	Bedtime
7 am	8.45 am	7 pm
11 am	12.45 pm	
3 pm	**Nap**	**Dreamfeed**
6.30 pm	4.30	10.30 pm

7 am

Wake your baby up and feed her. You will wake and feed her even if she last fed at 5.30 am, so she is always starting her day at the same time and on a full tummy.

8.45 am

Swaddle your baby and put her in bed on her back awake and allow her to self-settle (see guide to self-settling starting on page 187).

11 am

Wake your baby up and feed her.

12.45 pm

Swaddle your baby and put her in bed on her back awake and allow her to self-settle.

3 pm

Wake your baby up and feed her.

4.30 pm

Take your baby for a walk or out in the car to encourage her to sleep in places other than her bed.

5.15 pm
Wake your baby up and bath her, or give top-to-toe wash.

6.30 pm
Give your baby a feed. If you are breastfeeding and choose to give a bottle of expressed milk at this time, you will need to express 90 ml (3 oz) from each breast at 7.30 pm.

7 pm
Swaddle your baby and put her in bed on her back awake and allow her to self-settle.

10.30 pm
Give your baby a dreamfeed.

Night feeds
Feed your baby when she wakes during the night. During night feeds, try not to talk to her and keep the lights dim so she starts to understand the difference between night and day.

Routine for a baby aged ten weeks until yo[...] introduce solids

This routine is for a baby aged 70 days old until you introduc[...]

Feed times	Sleep times	Bedtime
7 am	9 am	7 pm
11 am	1 pm	
3 pm	**Nap**	**Dreamfeed**
6.30 pm	4.30 pm	10.30 pm

7 am

Wake your baby up and feed her. You will wake and feed her even if she last fed at 5.30 am, so she is always starting her day at the same time and on a full tummy.

9 am

Swaddle your baby and put her in bed on her back awake and allow her to self-settle (see guide to self-settling starting on page 187).

11 am

Wake your baby up and feed her.

1 pm

Swaddle your baby and put her in bed on her back awake and allow her to self-settle.

3 pm

Wake your baby up and feed her.

4.30 pm

Take your baby for a walk or out in the car to encourage her to sleep in places other than her bed. Don't worry if she doesn't as some babies only nap at this time every other day.

5.15 pm
Wake your baby up if necessary and bath her, or give top-to-toe wash.

6.30 pm
Give your baby a feed.

7 pm
Swaddle your baby and put her in bed on her back awake and allow her to self-settle.

10.30 pm
Give your baby a dreamfeed.

Night feeds
Feed your baby when she wakes during the night. During night feeds, try not to talk to her and keep the lights dim so she starts to understand the difference between night and day.

Tips:

- Your baby may sleep less than the recommended sleep time and this may vary slightly from day to day.

- Your baby does not have to have every scheduled sleep in her bed. If you have things to do, then you can let her sleep in the car or pram. What you do need to do is make sure your baby is in a safe and comfortable place to sleep at the times she is meant to be sleeping.

- When feeding at night, make sure you keep the lights dim and avoid eye contact or talking. Only change your baby's nappy if absolutely necessary.

- If you have no luck with my advice and routines, your baby could be suffering from reflux or have a dairy or other food allergy or intolerance. You should seek medical advice.

- If your baby dozes off between her last scheduled sleep and the next sleep time she may do so, but not in her bed.

- If your baby is younger than ten weeks and you notice her catnapping try keeping her up twenty minutes longer before her morning and afternoon sleep. If this does not work, you can rule out hunger as the cause of catnapping.

- If your baby takes longer than the allocated time for the bed-time feed then start the feed earlier. Don't delay the 7 pm bedtime.

- Some babies will want to move through the routines faster than scheduled—to read more information on this please see page 127.

THE EXCEPTIONS TO THE ROUTINES

Out of every hundred babies I meet, there is one family or baby that can't fit in with my routines. This can happen for a few reasons, the most common being another child in the family around whom the baby's routine needs to fit. A less-common reason might be a baby only ever sleeps one and a half hours in the morning and just can't last until the next scheduled sleep without getting really overtired. Below are two case studies to help you adjust the routine if you have one of these situations.

Emily's story

Vanessa wanted to use my routines with her second baby, ten-week-old Emily, but as her first child, Rebecca, was six, she had commitments such as the school run to do and was finding it hard to adjust. I asked her for the daily routine of her six-year-old and worked Emily's routine around it as follows. At 6.45 am Vanessa would get Emily up and feed her, finishing by about 7.15 am, which gave her just over an hour to get Rebecca up, dressed and fed for school. While she did all of this Emily was in her bouncy chair watching or playing under her baby gym. At 8.45 am they all went in the car to school, Emily usually napping for about ten minutes on the way before being lifted to take Rebecca to her classroom. This ten-minute nap was enough to get Emily by until she was put in bed at about 9.15 am. If on the odd occasion Emily fell back to sleep in the car on the way home, Vanessa would either sit in the car and read a book, make phone calls or bring Emily into the house in her car seat. At 10.30 am Emily would be woken for a feed, but instead of putting Emily back to bed at 12.30 pm, I suggested Emily go to bed at 12.15 pm to make up some extra sleep because her morning sleep was interrupted. At 2.30 pm Emily was given her next feed, but often Vanessa would get Emily up and go to the school first, so she could sit and feed her in the school playground waiting for Rebecca to come out of class. Vanessa found it easier to get Emily to wait the extra ten minutes before the feed so she could take her time feeding her, rather than feel she had to rush the feed to make it out the door in time for the school pick-up.

Vanessa would take both girls to the park at 4 pm and Emily would nap in the pram. The girls would have their bath at 5.30 pm and at 6.15 pm Emily would have her feed and be in bed for the night at 6.45 pm, with a dreamfeed at 10.15 pm.

Niamh's story

Samantha contacted me when her baby Niamh was twelve weeks. She had followed my routines since Niamh was born, and she was now sleeping twelve hours at night and went down for all her sleeps and naps without a fuss, with the exception of her 1 pm sleep. At this sleep Niamh would scream the house down and then only sleep for 40 minutes and get up screaming again. We finally worked out that Niamh had always woken up at 10.30 am from her morning sleep and just talked in her cot until she was picked up for her feed at 11 am so the screaming at 1 pm could be due to overtiredness, as by this stage Niamh had been up for two and a half hours. So I suggested Samantha try putting Niamh down at 12.30 pm for her afternoon sleep and see what happened. Niamh went down that and every day since without a fuss, sleeping until her 3 pm feed. I have since tried this with a handful of other babies who were having a similar problem and found it to work.

COMMON QUESTIONS

I would like to follow your routines with my two-week-old baby but I can't seem to express. How should I adjust the routines? I do not recommend any mother who is breastfeeding and not expressing to follow my routines in the first eight weeks. Expressing in this period ensures you will have enough milk during the growth spurts which happen at about three and six weeks through careful 'management' of the extra breastmilk expressing encourages. There are two reasons you need to express while on my routines: first, if you don't follow my expressing advice you might not have enough milk to give your baby during a growth spurt and, second, if you do not express as per my guidelines it might affect your milk supply. If you do not want to express, my advice is to start the routines after eight weeks.

Why do you advise not to put a baby in her bed to sleep at some points in your routines? I believe in giving a baby very clear messages. If you know your baby is tired and due a sleep, put her in her bed. The message your baby will start to learn is that her bed is a place for sleep, and you should get in the habit of only getting her up when she has slept. But at other points in the routine, I suggest your baby may only need a nap, and it's also possible that she won't sleep. At these times I recommend putting her down in a safe, comfortable place so, if she doesn't sleep, you may get her up without sending mixed messages.

We often go to my parents' or a friend's house for dinner – does the 7 pm bedtime mean this is out of the question? Don't worry – you can still have a life when following a routine! Perhaps you could go to the house where you are going to spend the evening early, so you can feed and settle your baby to sleep there. Put your baby down at 7 pm as normal, then try to leave for home so you arrive just in time for the dreamfeed, then put her in her own bed.

I am trying to get my fifteen-week-old breastfed baby into your routines, but she wants to feed every three hours. How can I stretch her feeds out? At first, changing a baby's habits can be hard, but it normally only takes a day to get a baby happily on my routines. I find the first four hours can be a problem and then the rest of the feeds fall into place easily. Get your baby up at 7 am and give her the first feed of the day. If she wakes up from her sleep and she is asking for food, try to distract with a walk or looking at different things in the house. If she is getting very upset you could swaddle and cuddle her, maybe even try singing to her. You might even find she falls back to sleep. Some parents use a dummy to stretch a baby for the first four hours. When 11 am comes you will find your baby will take a bigger feed and get to the 3 pm feed with little or no fuss.

What do I do at night if my baby wakes up before the dreamfeed? If your baby wakes within half an hour of the dreamfeed you should feed her. If there is over half an hour to the dreamfeed when she wakes you should resettle your baby.

What is the difference between a sleep and a nap? A sleep is for more than one sleep cycle, so it is usually over 40 minutes. But a nap is one sleep cycle or less.

What if my two-week-old daughter is not showing tired signs when you say to put her down for a sleep? You should still put her to bed as quite often, by the time you have waited for tired signs, your baby will be overtired making self-settling even harder.

When my baby wakes during the night for a feed, how long should I feed her? You should always feed your baby until she doesn't want any more.

I would like to start my fifteen-week-old on your routines, but she has been sleeping from 7 pm to 6.30 am every morning without the dreamfeed – should I still introduce it? If your baby has been sleeping all night without the dreamfeed then no, you shouldn't introduce it. But if, as your baby gets older, she starts waking at night again, you will need to either introduce solids (if she's over four months old) or give her the dreamfeed.

6

THE WEANING
PROCESS

The topic of when to wean your baby to solids is one I hear debated often by parents and health professionals. The Department of Health's current guideline at the time of publishing this book is to introduce solids at six months. I do not agree with this advice and recommend you start your baby on solids between four and four and a half months. I have researched the subject and found that unless your baby weighs less than 5.5 kg (12.1 lb), or there are medical reasons, four and a half months is the latest age for starting solids. It is also my opinion that solids should never be given to a baby weighing less than 5.5 kg (12.1 lb) who shows no signs of needing anything apart from breastmilk or formula. I believe that within a couple of years the Department of Health will change their guideline for introducing solids back to four months.

There are a few reasons for my strong opinion on this but the first is, in the past two years, I have had more and more parents contact me with babies who had slept well in the day and through the night, with a dreamfeed, from as early as six weeks but by five and a half months they were catnapping, night waking, irritable, crying and grumpy all day. I believe these babies would have stayed happy, contented and sleeping well if solids had been introduced at four months. It is my opinion that asking parents to delay the introduction of solids is an unrealistic goal and setting them up to fail.

My second reason for recommending you do not delay the introduction of solids to six months is to avoid allergies and fussy eating. International and national allergy bodies produce mounting evidence that if you delay the introduction of solids the incidence of food allergies rises dramatically. Starting solids between four and six months reduces a baby's risk of developing food allergies as the early introduction of different foods allows a baby to develop a tolerance. Delaying solids until six or seven months increases a baby's risk of having food allergies. Over the years I have noticed that babies introduced to a wide range of non-allergy-forming foods between the ages of four and four and a half months accepted a wider range of foods at one year than babies introduced to solids after four and a half months. I have also linked starting solids later than this to problems such as fussy eating, food and texture refusal, catnapping and repeated night waking. I believe that after six months a baby needs nutrition from other sources but if at six months he has only just been introduced to solids, your baby will still only be having a 'taste' and not getting enough to meet all of his nutritional needs.

I believe there is so much conflicting advice because the World Health Organisation (WHO) recommends solids not be introduced until a baby is six months old. However, the WHO guidelines were designed to protect babies in developing countries from gastro-infections as the water used to prepare their solids is more likely to be contaminated. In developed countries like the United Kingdom and Ireland introducing solids earlier does not carry these same risks.

Another cause for confusion around the age for starting babies on solid foods is the WHO recommends exclusive breastfeeding for the first six months of a baby's life. Some people believe this means babies shouldn't be given solids until they are six months but the real aim is to recommend that babies receive breastmilk only, rather than breastmilk and formula. Another benefit in introducing solids at four months is it can help keep breastfeeding going longer. When a mum goes back to work her baby can be offered some solids with expressed breastmilk in it rather than a bottle of formula.

Despite all these factors, the best way of deciding when to start solids is to go by your baby. If, for example, he is on the 'ten weeks until you introduce solids' routine and his day and night-time sleeps have slowly started to become shorter, this is a good indicator your baby is ready. My routines always give the milk feed first as it is important for a baby up to one year to get his full daily milk intake.

> **Tip:** You should never introduce solids before four months. Introducing solids before four months can damage your baby's digestive system as it takes up to four months to develop a gut lining strong enough to cope with solids while the kidneys are still not mature enough to handle the extra waste.

WHAT FOODS ARE SAFE – AND WHEN?

The following is a rough guide using my own experiences and the recommendations of different healthcare systems around the world. Always ask your health professional if unsure.

The information is broken up into different age groups to make planning and shopping easier. There is also a list in the appendix in alphabetical order for a parent to look up a food and see if it is suitable for their child.

Important note: Please be aware that the ages on this guide are based on a baby starting solids at four months. If your baby starts solids at five months, you will need to add one month to all the recommended ages (for example, asparagus should not be introduced until eight months, not seven months as listed). Keep this in mind also if purchasing commercial baby foods.

First foods – by age

From 4 months

Apples: Peeled, cored, cooked and given as a purée.
Butternut squash: Cooked and given as a purée.
Carrots: Cooked and given as a purée.
Courgette: Cooked and given as a purée.
Pears: Cooked and given as a purée.
Potatoes: Cooked and given as a purée.
Rice-based infant cereal
Swede: Cooked and given as a purée.

From 5 months
Beans (green): Cooked and given as a purée.
Sweet potato: Cooked and given as a purée.
Turnip: Cooked and given as a purée.

From 6 months
Apricots: Stoned, cooked and given as a purée.
Avocado: Mashed.
Bananas: Raw as a purée (look out for constipation).
Broccoli: Cooked and given as a purée.
Butter: In a small amount while cooking.
Cauliflower: Cooked and given as a purée.
Cheese: Give in very small amounts initially and watch for a reaction.
Chicken: Puréed in a casserole.
Fish: Look out for a reaction.
Lamb: In a casserole.
Lentils
Mango: Raw, mashed or puréed.
Oats: In a breakfast cereal.
Peaches: Cooked and given as a purée.
Peas: Cooked and given as mash or purée.

From 7 months
Asparagus: As a finger food.
Couscous
Peppers: In casseroles.
Rice: Cooked.
Spinach: Cooked.
Wheat-based infant cereal: Look out for a reaction.
Yoghurt: Look out for a reaction.

From 8 months
Apricots: raw from 8 months, cooked from 6 months.
Beans (pulses): I find they cause wind and some babies find them hard to digest.
Brussels sprouts: Be careful as can cause an upset tummy.

Cabbage
Dried fruit (currants, raisins, sultanas)
Leek
Melon: As a finger food.
Onion: Remove skins, dice and cook in casseroles.
Parsnips: Cooked and mashed.
Pasta: From when your baby is eating finger foods.
Pumpkin: Cooked and mashed.
Rhubarb: Cooked and mashed.
Sweet corn: Don't be surprised if you find it in your baby's nappy!
Tomatoes: Raw, skinned and seeded.
Vegetable oil: In cooking.

From 9 months
Aubergine: In a meal.
Beef: In casseroles.
Beetroot: In a meal.
Egg yolk: Hard-boiled – look out for a reaction.
Figs
Garlic: In very small amounts.
Liver: In small amounts (to my amazement, lots of babies like it!)
Mushrooms: In casseroles.
Prunes

From 10 months
Bread: Try a small amount of wheat in breakfast cereal first. The reason I say not to give bread is because your baby can make it into a ball and choke on it.
Cucumber: As a finger food.

From 12 months
Bean sprouts: As a finger food.
Berries: Be careful with strawberries as some babies may react.
Egg whites: Look out for a reaction.
Fruits: Unless individually listed otherwise.

Honey: But see note below.
Lettuce: Can be given raw.
Pineapple: As a finger food.
Plums: In very small amounts – look out for a reaction.

From 14 months

Cow's milk: Cow's milk is not suitable as a baby's main source of milk until he is over fourteen months. Your baby needs breastmilk or formula which provides all the correct nutrition until he is eating a variety of foods. Some say that cow's milk can be introduced at twelve months but the reason I recommend delaying to fourteen months is many clients find, when they first introduce it in cooked food or as a milk feed, their baby wakes up during the night or 40 minutes after they first go to sleep. If this happens I suggest you cut cow's milk out of your baby's diet and try it again a couple of months later. Start with small amounts in food and build it up until your baby can tolerate it.

From 18 months

Celery: As a finger food.
Shellfish: Look out for a reaction.

From 2½ years

Corn on the cob: Not recommended until your child has a full set of teeth.
Custard: Contains eggs so watch for a reaction. I have linked custard to sleep problems. This includes homemade versions.

From 5 years

Nuts: I would *never* give whole nuts to a child earlier than this – see note below.
Kiwifruit and grapefruit: can cause an allergic reaction.

These foods are DANGEROUS to some young children:

- Honey: There is some danger of infection from botulinum spores.

- Tea: The tannin and other compounds in tea can affect the absorption of iron.

- Nuts: Avoid all foods containing nuts, including spreads, if there are any allergies in your family. Even if there are no allergies in your family it's wise to avoid spreads containing nuts until your child is five. I believe you do not want to risk introducing nuts of any form until your child is old enough to comprehend the risks. Nut allergies are becoming more common and can cause very serious reactions. Whole nuts should never be given to a child younger than five as they can inhale them, choke on them or even stick them in their nose or ears.

- Grapes: Please do not give whole grapes to children under the age of five years. Ensure grapes are cut in half as whole grapes are a choking hazard to babies and young children.

Salt and Sugar

Both salt and sugar should be avoided when weaning. Giving sugar too often in the first two years of your baby's life could encourage a sweet tooth and the refusing of savoury food. Your baby will get all the sugar he needs from fruit. Sugar is often listed in commercial baby foods as one of the following: dextrose, sucrose, glucose or fructose.

Salt should never be added to food for a baby or child under two years old as it can put too much pressure on a baby's immature kidneys. If you are preparing a meal for the whole family, take out the baby's portion before adding the salt. Watch out for hidden salt in things like adult breakfast cereal.

Tip: I am not a big fan of commercial baby foods, having come across quite a few sleep problems over the years with babies who have only been fed them. I think often babies don't get enough calories from these foods and then wake at night looking for more to eat. When their diet is changed to homemade food the night-waking disappears.

Some commercial foods are better than others. I don't see the problem in giving your baby things like plain fruit or vegetables from a jar with little else added. It is the meals in a jar that I find do not satisfy a baby's hunger. The other problem with commercial food is that older toddlers occasionally refuse to eat anything else and won't join in with family meals.

It is, however, a good idea to give your baby the odd jar of commercial baby food, just in case you ever need to travel or go somewhere where it is not hygienic or convenient to give home-cooked foods.

If you have a baby who will only eat commercial baby foods and you would like to get him to eat home-cooked foods, a good trick is to add a little home-cooked food into the commercial food at each meal time, slowly bringing the amount up until it is all home-cooked food.

CRASH COURSE IN WEANING

Days one to three
Rice cereal

Start the day in the normal way, following the routine for a baby aged ten weeks until solids are started. I recommend giving your baby his first taste of solids at around 12 noon, so if he has an allergic reaction it will be while you are awake.

Give your baby his 11 am feed as normal. Just before midday, mix one teaspoon of baby rice cereal with warmed expressed breastmilk or warmed formula. You could also use cool, boiled water but I find babies prefer the taste of the milk they are used to. You will need to mix it to a very smooth consistency. **Always test the temperature of any food before you give it to your baby.** Once you have tested it, put a little on a spoon and slowly put it against your baby's lips. When your baby opens his mouth a little, put the spoon in just far enough so you can slowly pull it out, wiping a little of its contents on his upper gum. This will encourage your baby to eat. Alternatively, some babies will like to suck the rice cereal off the spoon, so you may need to hold the spoon in their mouth for them. Don't worry if your baby is not keen at first. It sometimes takes up to twelve tastes of something for your baby to show interest. After he has had a couple of tastes, carry on with your daily routine as normal. Do this for three days.

Days four to six
Rice cereal and apple purée

I always introduce some apple purée on the fourth day to avoid baby getting constipated (introducing vegetables as well as rice cereal at this early stage may also cause constipation). Once again, follow the routine as normal but at 12 noon give a portion of apple purée. At around 5.15 pm give him his rice cereal followed by his bath, and then it's back on the routine.

Days seven to nine
Rice cereal and apple and carrot purées
Now it is time to start the routine for a baby on solids to six and a half months. This means two courses at each meal.

At 8 am give him rice cereal by itself or mixed with apple purée, and then offer some apple purée alone as a second course.

At noon give your baby some carrot purée, followed by apple purée alone or mixed with rice cereal as a second course.

At 5.20 pm give your baby some rice cereal, followed by apple purée as a second course.

Days ten to twelve
Rice cereal and apple, carrot and pear purées
Give your baby rice cereal at 8 am mixed with a new taste of pear purée. Now that he has a few tastes, you can mix these foods around a bit.

You could give rice at lunchtime and carrot and apple at dinnertime (I have found babies love this one).

Days thirteen to fifteen
Rice cereal and apple, pear, carrot and courgette purées
Introduce the courgette purée at 12 noon.

Days sixteen to eighteen
Rice cereal and apple, pear, carrot, courgette and swede purées
Introduce the swede purée at 12 noon.

Days nineteen to 21
Rice cereal and apple, pear, carrot, courgette, swede and potato purées
Introduce the potato purée at 12 noon.

I'm sure you get the idea. I have added some basic recipes below to help you.

CLASSIC PURÉES
When making fruit or vegetable purées, always take the skin off and remove all stones, cores and seeds. This includes tomatoes.

Pear purée (from 4 months)
Ingredients
2 medium pears
Method
Wash the pears under a running cold tap. Peel, core and dice the pears, taking care to remove all the pips. Place the pears in a small steaming basket (available at most supermarkets) over a saucepan of simmering water. Steam the fruit until soft (remember that over-cooking causes loss of nutrients). Remove pears and purée with a blender or food processor. You may need to add some water from the saucepan to get the correct consistency. Allow the purée to cool before spooning into clean ice-cube trays. Cover the trays and place in freezer. After four hours, pop the cubes of frozen pear into a labelled and dated freezer bag. You now have serving-size portions ready to be defrosted in the fridge or microwave. Make apple purée using the same method.

Carrot purée (from 4 months)
Ingredients
2 large carrots
Method
Wash the carrots under a running cold tap. Peel and chop the carrots, taking care to remove the top and tail. Place the carrots in steaming basket and steam until tender (remember that over-cooking causes loss of nutrients). Remove carrots and purée with a blender or food processor. You may need to add some water from the saucepan to get the correct consistency. Allow the purée to cool before spooning into clean ice-cube trays. Cover the trays and place in freezer. After four hours, pop the cubes of carrot into a labelled and dated freezer bag. You now have serving-size portions ready to be defrosted in the fridge or microwave. Make courgette, swede, potato and sweet potato purée using the same method. You could also use expressed breastmilk or formula to thin the purée if necessary.

COMMON QUESTIONS
Why do you introduce baby rice cereal first? Baby rice cereal is

very bland, so mixing it with the milk your baby is used to will make the transition to solid food easier. I always suggest introducing some puréed apple or pear next to avoid your baby getting constipated.

What is food intolerance? Is it the same as an allergy? No, it is not the same as a food allergy and many people confuse the two. Food intolerance does not involve the immune system. It is a reaction to certain natural or added chemicals in a baby's or a breastfeeding mother's diet. For example, a chemical known to cause food intolerance is salicylate, which is found in cheese, chocolate, fish, yeast extracts, bananas, avocados and tomatoes. Monosodium glutamate (MSG) is another one, along with additives such as tartrazine and sulphites. Symptoms of food intolerances include tiredness, tummy pains, diarrhoea, hives and headaches. Babies suffering from food intolerance are usually very irritable and hard to settle. Food intolerances are difficult to diagnose, so if you suspect your baby is suffering from food intolerances, see your doctor or a dietician.

How much milk should my baby drink? A newborn baby drinks approximately 600 ml (20 oz) of milk daily; a four- to six-month-old approximately 1000 ml (34 oz) daily; a six- to twelve-month-old approximately 600 to 700 ml (20 to 24 oz) daily; and a child of one to three years should still drink about 600 ml (20 oz) of milk a day.

How will I know my baby is still getting enough milk when I introduce solids? Up until six months, milk is the most important food for your baby. Your baby will still be getting enough if you are following my routines as the milk feeds are given first. This means your baby will fill his tummy with milk before food.

When can I give my baby breakfast cereal? You may give your baby oat cereal from six months. It is best to give some fruit with the cereal. All the cereals you give your baby should be wheat and gluten free until he is nine months old. Commercial breakfast cereals should not be given until your baby is over a year as they contain salt. Be careful to read ingredients before giving your baby commercial foods.

My health visitor has advised me to move my baby's milk and solid feeds around so I am giving solids first. What do you think? I come across this time and time again and am still not sure why some advisers recommend this change. With my routines, the solids are already at proper meal times so if they were swapped with milk feed, you would be giving lunch at 11 am and dinner at 4 pm. Some of my clients have made this change only to find their babies start to wake again in the night. I believe that by giving the milk an hour before, by the time you give your baby his solids the milk is nearly digested, leaving more room for the solids. But when you turn it around and give the milk second, the solids are not yet digested so the baby does not take as much milk.

Why do some babies move through the routines faster than others? There appear to be two reasons for this. Larger babies often need more awake time. In an ideal world, the routines would be separated by weight rather than age, but that would have made things very complicated, especially when moving to stages like solids and fewer milk feeds. Also, babies that are on the routines from day one often need less sleep than babies starting the routines later. Perhaps this is because these babies have never had sleep issues so don't have lost hours of sleep to catch up on!

What milk should I give my baby between one year and fourteen months (when you say to introduce cow's milk)? Is toddler formula okay? I advise you to avoid toddler formulas as some contain a large amount of sugar. This can have the same effect as introducing cow's milk before fourteen months in that it makes toddlers unsettled. You can give breastmilk to your baby at any age or, if he is drinking formula, I suggest you continue to use the infant ones until you introduce cow's milk after fourteen months.

7

ROUTINES FROM STARTING SOLIDS TO 24 MONTHS

ROUTINE FOR A BABY ON SOLIDS UNTIL SIX AND A HALF MONTHS

Feed times	Solids	Sleep times
7 am	8 am	9 am
11 am	12 noon	1 pm
3 pm	5.20 pm	4.30 pm (possible nap)
6.20 pm		
	Dreamfeed	**Bedtime**
	10.30 pm	7 pm

7 am
If your baby wakes before 7 am, delay her milk feed until 7 am as this will encourage her to sleep longer. Otherwise, wake her at 7 am and give her a milk feed.

8 am
Give your baby breakfast. Feed her until she turns her head away. I recommend you give her two courses, one savoury and one sweet.

9 am

Put your baby to bed awake and allow her to self-settle. This means without the help of you or a dummy.

11 am

Give your baby her milk feed. This feed will start to get smaller as she gets older and is eating more solids.

12 noon

Feed your baby two courses of solids, one savoury and one sweet.

1 pm

Put your baby to bed awake and allow her to self-settle.

3 pm

Wake your baby up and give her a milk feed.

4.30 pm

If your baby has not slept well, you might want to encourage a nap in the car or pram. At about six and a half months she no longer needs this nap.

5.20 pm

Feed your baby two courses of solids, one savoury and one sweet. If she is now skipping the nap at 4.30 pm, try giving solids at 5 pm to allow a bigger space before the milk feed.

6 pm

Bath your baby, or give top-to-toe wash.

6.20 pm

Give your baby her milk feed. She needs to finish this feed at least ten minutes before bedtime.

7 pm

Put your baby to bed fully awake and allow her to self-settle.

10.30 pm
Dreamfeed.

Note: If you are starting this routine with a baby over four months who is sleeping from 7 pm until 7 am without the dreamfeed (see page 84) you do not need to introduce it. However, if your baby starts to wake at 5 am you will need to either introduce the dreamfeed or solids. If there is no history of allergies in your family, I recommend you introduce solids rather than the dreamfeed.

Giving up the dreamfeed

Once your baby has been on solids for eight weeks and is sleeping through every night, it's time to drop the dreamfeed. The first thing you should do is bring the dreamfeed forward half an hour earlier for five nights; if your baby continues to sleep all night then bring the dreamfeed forward another half an hour earlier again for five nights – doing this every five nights until the dreamfeed is at 8 pm. If this still has no effect then, if your baby is bottle-fed, reduce the amount each night by 20 ml (0.7 oz) and for breastfed babies reduce the breastfeed by two minutes each night. When you are at the 30 ml (1 oz) or two minute stage don't do the dreamfeed again. If at any point your baby wakes earlier in the morning go back to feeding the amount of milk that you were giving at the time before the wake happened. Then try to reduce or move it again five days later.

Changing routines

For young babies I suggest you follow each of the routines for two weeks as stated until your baby reaches the routine for a baby aged ten weeks until introduction of solids. The majority of babies are happy on this routine until solids are introduced at four months. These babies then continue on with the starting solids to six and a half months routine before their next change. However there does seem to be a percentage of babies who like to move through the routines a little faster.

There appears to be two reasons for this. Larger babies often need more awake time. In an ideal world, the routines would be separated by weight rather than age, but that would have made things very complicated, especially when moving to stages like solids and fewer milk feeds. Also, babies that are on the routines from day one often need less sleep than babies starting the routines later. Perhaps this is because these babies have never had sleep issues so don't have lost hours of sleep to catch up on!

There are a few indicators that you can use to determine when it's time to change routines. If your baby begins rising before 7 am, takes a longer time than normal to settle (which includes playing the 'throwing the comforter away game' and sitting or standing in the cot) or begins catnapping, it may be time to move on to the next routine. However, please note I only recommend changing routines after you have ruled out hunger or coldness. Additionally, you may find you only need to move the afternoon sleep at first and your baby will remain happy with the earlier morning sleep for a while longer.

ROUTINE FOR A BABY AGED SIX AND A HALF TO NINE MONTHS

Feed times	Solids	Sleep times
7 am	8 am	9.20 am
11 am	12 pm	1.20 pm
When she wakes	5 pm	
6.30 pm		**Bedtime**
		7 pm

7 am
If your baby wakes before 7 am, delay her milk feed until 7 am as this will encourage her to sleep longer. Otherwise, wake your baby at 7 am and give her a milk feed.

8 am
Give your baby breakfast. Remember to feed her until she turns her head away. I recommend you give her two courses.

9.20 am
Put your baby to bed awake and allow her to self-settle. This means without the help of you or a dummy.

11 am
Give your baby her milk feed. This feed will start to get smaller as your baby gets older and is eating more solids. If you are worried about your baby's milk intake add expressed breastmilk or formula to her solid meals.

12 pm
Feed your baby two courses of solids for lunch, one savoury and one sweet.

1.20 pm
Put your baby to bed for a sleep. When she wakes, give her a milk feed. Do not let her day sleep add up in total to more than four hours.

5 pm

Feed your baby two courses of solids, one savoury and one sweet.

6 pm

Bath your baby, or give top-to-toe wash.

6.30 pm

Give your baby her full milk feed. She needs to finish this feed at least ten minutes before bedtime. If this feed usually takes longer then start it earlier.

7 pm

Put your baby to bed fully awake.

ROUTINE FOR A BABY AGED NINE TO TWELVE MONTHS

Feed times	Solids	Sleep times
7 am	8 am	9.50 am
When she wakes	One hour after	Three hours after
When she wakes	her milk feed	she woke
6.30 pm	5 pm	
		Bedtime
		7 pm

7 am
If your baby wakes before 7 am, delay her milk feed until 7 am as this will encourage her to sleep longer. Otherwise, wake your baby at 7 am and give her a milk feed.

8 am
Give your baby breakfast. Remember to feed her until she turns her head away. I recommend you give her two courses.

9.50 am
Put your baby to bed awake and allow her to self-settle. This means without the help of you or a dummy. Let her sleep until she wakes up. When she wakes feed her half the amount of milk she usually has at 7 am, or feed her for half the time at the breast.

One hour after she woke up
Feed your baby two courses of solids, one savoury and one sweet.

Three hours after she woke up
Put your baby to bed for a sleep. When she wakes, give half her normal-sized milk feed. Do not let her sleep past 4.15 pm.

5 pm
Feed your baby two courses of solids, one savoury and one sweet.

6 pm
Bath baby, or give top-to-toe wash.

6.30 pm
Give your baby her full milk feed. She needs to finish this feed at least ten minutes before bedtime. If this feed usually takes longer then start it earlier.

7 pm
Put your baby to bed fully awake.

If your baby is nearly a year old and finding it harder to get to sleep at 9.50 am, she may be ready for a change in routine and this needs to happen gradually. I recommend you put her down a little later every five or more days until you find the times she is happy to have day sleeps.

From twelve months it is harder for you to follow my routines exactly because babies of this age all have slightly different sleep needs. You will need to watch your baby and when she starts to take longer to fall asleep or starts to catnap at a sleep, this is the sign she needs to move to the next routine. From here I have given you some routines which are based on what the average baby of each age is doing.

At one year old your baby is ready to start dropping milk feeds. Firstly the half feeds that are after the morning and afternoon sleeps should be reduced slowly over a few days until they are gone. Then it is up to you if you would like to drop the other feeds. If you choose to give up the other two milk feeds or replace them with a cup of milk then the first milk feed you should drop is the morning one. The last feed to go, or be replaced by a cup, is the 6.30 pm feed.

SAMPLE ROUTINE FOR A BABY AGED TWELVE MONTHS

Feed times	Solids	Sleep times
7 am	8 am	10.15 am
6.40 pm	12.30 pm	Three hours and
	5 pm	twenty minutes after
		she woke
		Bedtime
		7 pm

7 am

If your baby wakes before 7 am, delay her milk feed until 7 am as this will encourage her to sleep longer. Otherwise, wake your baby at 7 am and give her a milk feed.

8 am

Give your baby breakfast. Remember to feed her until she turns her head away. I recommend you give your baby two courses, one savoury and one sweet.

10 am

Give your baby morning tea – some fruit or a biscuit and a drink of water or milk.

10.15 am

Put your baby to bed awake and allow her to self-settle. This means without the help of you or a dummy.

12.30 pm

Do not wake your baby if she is still asleep. Let her sleep as long as she wants to. Give her lunch when she wakes up.

Three hours and twenty minutes after she woke up

Put your baby to bed for a sleep. Do not let her sleep past 4.15 pm.

5 pm

Give your baby a dinner of two courses.

6 pm

Bath baby, or give top-to-toe wash.

6.40 pm

Give your baby her full milk feed (if you are still giving it). She needs to finish this feed at least ten minutes before bedtime. If this feed usually takes longer start it earlier.

7 pm

Put your baby down to bed fully awake and allow her to self-settle.

SAMPLE ROUTINE FOR A BABY AGED FOURTEEN MONTHS

Feed times	Solids	Sleep times
7 am	8 am	10.45 am
6.40 pm	1 pm	Three hours and
	5 pm	40 minutes after
		she woke
		Bedtime
		7 pm

7 am

If your baby wakes before 7 am, delay her milk feed until 7 am as this will encourage her to sleep longer. Otherwise, wake her at 7 am and give her a milk feed.

8 am

Give your baby breakfast. Remember to feed her until she turns her head away. I recommend you give your baby two courses, one savoury and one sweet.

10 am

Give your baby morning tea – some fruit or a biscuit and a drink of water or milk.

10.45 am

Put your baby to bed awake and allow her to self-settle. This means without the help of you or a dummy.

1 pm

Do not wake your baby if she is still asleep. Let her sleep as long as she wants to. Give your baby lunch when she wakes up. If she sleeps over 2½ hours then she does not need a second sleep.

Three hours and 40 minutes after she woke up
Put your baby to bed for a sleep. Do not let her sleep past 4.15 pm.

5 pm
Give your baby dinner.

6 pm
Bath baby, or give top-to-toe wash.

6.40 pm
Give your baby her full milk feed (if you are still giving it). She needs to finish this feed at least ten minutes before bedtime. If this feed usually takes longer start it earlier.

7 pm
Put your baby down to bed fully awake and allow her to self-settle.

SAMPLE ROUTINE FOR A TODDLER AGED SIXTEEN MONTHS

7 am
Some toddlers have given up the morning milk drink by this age, but if your toddler is interested, I still recommend it as the milk is very important for her bones. If she wakes before 7 am, delay milk or breakfast until 7 am. If she does not wake before 7 am, don't wake her if you don't need to. When your toddler wakes up, start the morning with either her milk feed or breakfast. If you are still giving a milk feed, give breakfast one hour after the milk.

10 am
Give your toddler morning tea – some fruit or a biscuit and a drink of water or milk.

11.30 am
Give your toddler something to eat, as this will most likely be the time she has lunch for the next couple of months.

12 noon
Put your toddler to bed awake and allow her to self-settle.

2.30 pm
Do not let your toddler sleep for more than two and a half hours. When she wakes up she will need something to eat and drink. What and how much will depend on when and how much she ate at lunch.

5 pm
Give your toddler dinner.

6 pm
Bath your toddler, or give top-to-toe wash.

6.40 pm
Give your toddler her milk drink from breast, bottle or cup.

7 pm
Put your toddler to bed fully awake and allow her to self-settle.

SAMPLE ROUTINE FOR A TODDLER AGED EIGHTEEN MONTHS

7 am

Some toddlers have given up the morning milk drink by this age, but if your toddler is interested, I still recommend it as the milk is very important for her bones. If she wakes before 7 am, delay milk or breakfast until 7 am. If she does not wake before 7 am, don't wake her if you don't need to. When your toddler wakes up, start the morning with either her milk feed or breakfast. If you are still giving a milk drink, give breakfast one hour after the milk.

10 am

Give your toddler morning tea – some fruit or a biscuit and a drink of water or milk.

12 noon

Give your toddler some lunch.

12.45 pm

Put your toddler to bed awake and allow her to self-settle.

2.45 pm

Do not let your toddler sleep for more than two hours. When she wakes up she will need something to eat and drink.

5 pm

Give your toddler dinner.

Please see page 143 for the bedtime ritual.

SAMPLE ROUTINE FOR A TODDLER AGED 24 MONTHS UNTIL THE DAYTIME NAP HAS GONE

7 am
Some toddlers have given up the morning milk drink by this age, but if your toddler is interested, I still recommend it as the milk is very important for her bones. If she wakes before 7 am, delay milk or breakfast until 7 am. If she does not wake before 7 am, don't wake her if you don't need to. When your toddler wakes up, start the morning with either her milk feed or breakfast. If you are still giving a milk drink, give breakfast one hour after the milk.

10 am
Give your toddler morning tea – some fruit or a biscuit and a drink of water or milk.

12.20 pm
Give your toddler some lunch.

1 pm
Put your toddler to bed awake and allow her to self-settle. If she starts to take a long time to settle for her day sleep or starts to throw her comforter out of her cot, try putting her to bed twenty minutes later. The latest I would recommend you put her to bed is 2.45 pm.

Your toddler will reach a stage where she will no longer need a sleep or nap during the day. At this stage a rest is a good idea until she is about four years old. If she stops sleeping at this time, you can make it a rest time by giving her a few books to read in bed.

Two hours after you put your toddler to bed or 3.30 pm
Wake your toddler up two hours after she went to bed or at 3.30 pm whichever is earlier. Do not let her sleep past 3.30 pm regardless of when she went to sleep. Offer her a drink and a small afternoon snack.

5 pm
Give your toddler dinner.

THE BEDTIME RITUAL

6 pm
Bath your toddler, or give a top-to-toe wash.

6.30 pm
Give your toddler her milk drink from the breast, bottle or cup. If you would like to read a story to your little one this is the time to do it, but it's best to ensure that both the story and the milk feed are over by 6.40 pm.

6.40 pm
Have active play time out of your toddler's bedroom.

6.55 pm
Brush your toddler's teeth.

6.59 pm
Say goodnight to a few toys and pop your toddler in her safe sleeping bag and into her cot, then tuck her in under sheets and blankets. Say goodnight and walk out of the bedroom, allowing her to settle himself.

A NEW BABY WITH A TODDLER ON A ROUTINE

Below is a sample routine to help you adjust my routines for a household with a toddler and a new baby.

SAMPLE ROUTINE FOR A TWENTY-MONTH-OLD TODDLER AND A TEN-WEEK-OLD BABY

Baby feed times	Toddler meal times	Baby sleep times	Toddler sleep times
7 am	8 am: breakfast	9 am	
11 am	10 am: morning tea	12.45 pm	12.45 pm
3 pm	12 noon: lunch	4.30 pm: nap	
6.30 pm	5 pm: dinner	7 pm: bedtime	7 pm: bedtime
10.30 pm: dreamfeed			

7 am

Wake your baby up and feed her. If your toddler wakes before 7 am, delay giving her milk drink until 7 am. If she is still asleep, let her wake in her own time.

8 am

Give your toddler her breakfast.

9 am

Aim to have somewhere to go each morning where your toddler can burn some energy and you can let your baby have her morning sleep in her pram.

10 am

Give your toddler morning tea.

11 am

Wake your baby up and feed her.

12 noon
Give your toddler lunch.

12.45 pm
Aim to put both your toddler and baby down at 12.45 pm each day so you get a break. If your baby has had a good two-hour sleep in the morning then keep her up until 1 pm.

2.45 pm
Wake your toddler up and give her a snack and a drink of milk or water.

3 pm
Wake your baby up and feed her.

4 pm
Take both baby and toddler out – maybe to the park, so your baby can nap and your toddler can burn a little more energy!

5 pm
Give your toddler dinner.

5.15 pm
Wake your baby up from her nap if necessary.

6 pm
Bath your children.

6.30 pm
Give your baby a feed and your toddler a drink of milk.

6.50 pm
Read both your baby and your toddler a story before putting them to bed.

7 pm
Swaddle your baby and put her in bed on her back awake and allow her to self-settle. Then put your toddler to bed.

10.30 pm
Give your baby a dreamfeed.

Night feeds
Feed your baby when she wakes during the night. During night feeds, try not to talk to her and keep the lights dim, so she starts to understand the difference between night and day.

Tips:
- If you find your baby wakes each night at 4 am or 5 am, she is most likely cold as this is the coldest part of the night.

- By three years old your toddler should not need more than one and a half hours of day sleep, and this will turn into just rest time as she gets older. It is normal for your three-year-old to sleep every other day.

- Once your baby is sixteen months old, you do not need to wake her at 7 am. You can let her sleep in the morning until she wakes and then offer either her milk feed or breakfast when she wakes. However, if you find that by letting your baby sleep in past 7 am it starts to cause problems with her day sleep, then it may be best to go back to waking her at 7 am every morning.

COMMON QUESTIONS

I have been advised to cut my ten-month-old's milk feeds down to three but on your nine- to twelve-month routine there are still four milk feeds – is this okay? What looks like four scheduled milk feeds in this routine is actually three, because you will give two full feeds and two half feeds. At nine months, I find babies still need milk and cutting the feeds to three may mean your baby doesn't get enough. Spread over four feeds, with two 'half' ones, the recommended daily intake is reached.

My son has been on your routines since birth. He is now sixteen months and some days he is ready for bed at 9.30 am so I put him down at this time, but other days he is fine to stay awake until 12 noon. Am I confusing him by not doing the same each day? It often happens that a baby alternates between two different routines. This will not cause a problem if you stick to the same bedtimes and have two routines on alternate days, or even one routine for two days then the other for a day. It will become a problem if you keep changing the times, for example, one day putting him back to bed at 9.30 am, the next at 11.20 am and the next at 10 am.

My baby has been drinking water quite happily out of her sipper cup since she was eight months. Now that she is one, I have recently added full cow's milk to her cereal instead of breastmilk. She takes the cow's milk in her cereal well, but refuses it from a cup – how can I get her to take it? Try adding a little bit of cow's milk into her water, starting with one teaspoon of milk per cup and slowly bringing the amount of milk up each day. This way she will gradually get used to the taste of the milk.

8

MULTIPLE LOVE AND EARLY ARRIVALS

Multiple births are a lot more common than most parents realise. In fact, one in forty births is a twin. Often when pregnant with more than one baby you do not carry to full term, so these babies are generally smaller and not as strong as the average. This makes it harder to follow my routines from the early days, and without talking to each one of you and finding out your individual needs, it is harder for me to advise you. So this chapter shares some of the advice and routines I have used in the past but will only be a guide; you will have to look at your own individual needs and the needs of each of your babies before deciding on a routine for your family.

Having a premature baby is also very common. My son Darragh arrived nearly seven weeks premature and spent some time in a special care baby unit, so I have firsthand experience as a parent on this subject. If you have a premature baby you will find much of the advice I give to parents of multiples will also apply to you.

I have found over the years that parents with twins, triplets or quads often need less help from me than parents of children of different ages or even of single babies. Perhaps this is because they prepare themselves 'for the worst' and decide to be organised and on a good sleep and feeding routine from day one.

WHERE SHOULD YOUR BABIES SLEEP?

Many parents of multiple-birth babies choose to sleep them in the same cot. In fact, research shows that they are more likely to settle well if in close contact with each other as they were in the womb. But the downside to this is that at some point you will need to separate your babies, particularly when one or all of them start to roll or get mobile. Unfortunately, the longer they sleep together the harder it will be for them to learn to settle apart.

I advise putting your babies in separate cots which are set up as close to each other as possible. This way they will be able to talk to and see each other but there is no risk of an accident and no separation issues later.

FEEDING

Sometimes with babies born early it's not possible to breastfeed them from the beginning. Often these babies are fed by tube or parents are advised to give their feeds from a bottle until the babies are strong enough to suck from the breast. If you find this to be the case for you, try to express and give your babies expressed breastmilk. This will also keep your supply up for when your babies are strong enough to breastfeed. You should express every three hours in the day and four hours in the night to keep up a good milk supply.

There is no reason why you would not be able to breastfeed more than one baby, and over the years I have seen many mothers do so without experiencing any major problems. Most mothers are capable of producing enough milk for more than one baby. But it's also important to look at both your individual situation and your family's needs. There is no point trying to breastfeed if you are finding yourself too tired to enjoy your babies, or if you spend all your time worrying about whether they are getting enough food. If you are concerned about this, talk to your health professional about their weight gain. If they are all gaining enough weight, settling and sleeping well, then you know you are producing enough milk. And remember, some breastmilk is better than none. With this in mind, a lot of my clients have decided to give a mixture of breastmilk and formula.

There are so many different approaches when it comes to feeding twins. Some mothers find it easier to breastfeed both babies at the same time, while others like to feed one at a time. If you are feeding both babies at the same time, follow my normal routines for your babies' ages (depending upon whether they are breast- or formula-fed). If you find feeding them separately easier then you can use my routines in this chapter as guides, but you may need to vary them for your babies' individual needs.

A guide to breastfeeding twins before your milk comes in

If breastfeeding twins together use the guide below until your milk comes in. If breastfeeding twins separately use the sample routine for breastfeeding twins separately aged one week and over 3 kg (6.6 lb) (page 154) and only put your babies on the breast for the length of time given on the chart below until your milk comes in.

	Baby A	Baby B
Day one: feed each baby every three hours from the breast you have allocated to that baby for the day	**Right breast for 10 minutes**	**Left breast for 10 minutes**
Day two: feed each baby every three hours but on the opposite breast to the day before (read my advice on alternating between breasts later in this chapter)	**Left breast for 16 minutes**	**Right breast for 16 minutes**
Day three: feed each baby from the allocated breast every three hours	**Right breast for 21 minutes**	**Left breast for 21 minutes**
Day four and every day until your milk comes in: feed each baby from the allocated breast every three hours	**Left breast for 28 minutes**	**Right breast for 28 minutes**

Note: If you have more than two babies you will need to ask a lactation consultant for breastfeeding advice.

Breastfeeding when your milk comes in

You will know as soon as your milk is coming in because your breasts will start to become fuller and harder. You will notice the colour of your milk changing from the yellow colostrum to a paler, slightly blue milky colour. Some women suffer from painful engorged breasts at this time but this is less likely to happen if you are following my guide.

I know my advice so far does not give your babies as much milk or sucking time as a single baby would at the same stage, but over the years I have seen so many mothers of twins not follow these simple guidelines in the first week and then end up in agony with bleeding and cracked nipples in week two. They then give up breastfeeding altogether because it all gets too hard. I strongly believe you are better off feeding your babies for less time initially to avoid these problems, and then go on to have a long breastfeeding experience with your babies.

From the day your milk comes in, usually day three to five, you should offer each baby one breast until it is completely empty at each feed. You will need to remember to feed one baby on one breast all day (see full explanation on page 158). You must encourage your babies to drain the breast they are feeding from so each baby is getting enough hindmilk. It may take up to 45 minutes for each baby to empty each breast, much longer than if you had one baby because your breasts will have more milk in them to meet the demand.

It is very important to feed every three hours during the day in the first two weeks. If you feed more often your babies may be snacking and never reaching that very important hindmilk. In the case of twins or more, you may need to use a dummy to help your babies last the three hours between feeds, but I advise getting rid of the dummies by week three or problems of dependency will start.

After your milk has come in, you can let your babies sleep up to five hours at night in the first two weeks. But wake your babies at the five-hour mark as it could affect your milk supply if your breasts go too long at night without being stimulated.

DISTURBING THE OTHER BABIES AT SLEEP TIMES

Many parents are overly worried that one baby will wake the other baby or babies in the same room, so they run to their babies every time they make the slightest sound. This is unnecessary and could potentially cause ongoing sleep problems in newborn babies. Babies usually have a much higher tolerance for nocturnal noise than their parents do and this is clearly shown with twins who rarely disturb each other when sharing a room. Twins represent particular challenges but for every challenge there is a solution.

I have gone to many homes to assist parents of twins in teaching their babies how to self-settle and sleep all night and seen examples where one of the babies will shout so loudly that the whole house is awake except for the twin that is asleep next to him.

If there is a problem of disturbance where two babies sleep in the same room, a tactic that can be tried is to use sleep cycles to your advantage and stagger the times that you put them to bed so that their cycles overlap each other. With the average sleep cycle lasting 40 minutes, putting the babies to sleep twenty to 25 minutes apart will avoid both coming into light sleep at the same time and disturbing each other.

NIGHT FEEDS

I have always told my clients to try to treat their babies as individuals at night. I don't believe it is fair to wake the second baby for a feed just because the first baby has woken and asked for one. I know this makes your life a bit harder because you have to get up again when the second baby wakes, especially if you have just got back to sleep, but it is worth it in the long run because you will find your babies will start to sleep all night sooner. Quite often with twins, I find one baby sleeps all night a week or two weeks sooner than the other. Remember, you should not let a breastfed baby go longer than five hours at night without a feed (or six hours for a bottle-fed baby until they have regained their birth weight and are over 3 kg / 6.6 lb). This means you should have alarm clocks set differently for each baby.

INTRODUCING SOLIDS

When to introduce solids can be an interesting question if you have more than one baby. Often one baby will be showing signs of being ready for solids well before the other baby or babies are ready to start.

If this happens to you, once again you need to look at your own circumstances. If the baby you feel is ready for solids has started to catnap in the day and is waking again at night, you really need to start him on solids. You could begin with rice cereal and apple until the time the other baby or babies are ready – it is not a good idea to move your first baby onto a variety of tastes without the other(s) because it will just get too confusing when trying to watch for allergies. Most parents with more than one baby feed all the babies from one bowl with one spoon. This is all right if your babies are well, but if one of them is sick or showing signs of a sickness, use different bowls and spoons for each baby.

WHEN IT COMES TO ROUTINES

As mentioned previously, many multiple babies are not carried to full term so are often born smaller than usual. If your babies are born early and you are breastfeeding them, I suggest you use my one- to two-week breastfeeding routine (page 154) as a guide until your babies are over 3 kg (6.6 lb) before advancing to my next routine. If you are bottle-feeding with breastmilk or formula, I suggest you use my newborn to two-week routine (page 162) until your babies are over 3 kg (6.6 lb). When they do reach this goal, follow each routine for two weeks. Once you reach the ten-week routine, your next change of routine will be when you start your babies on solids.

Below is a rough guide to when to start a premature baby on solids.

Number of weeks premature	The average age recommended to start solids
Four weeks	Seventeen weeks
Six weeks	Eighteen weeks
Eight weeks	Nineteen weeks
Ten weeks	Twenty weeks
Twelve weeks	21 weeks

> **Tip:** When feeding twins, I suggest alternating between breasts every 24 hours. Please look at the sample routine below for further details.

SAMPLES OF ADJUSTED ROUTINES FOR TWIN BABIES

You will notice the routines in this chapter I call sample routines. This is because you will need to look at your own babies' needs and create your own routines. Here are a couple of things to take into account when creating your own routines: does one baby feed longer than the other, does one take longer to burp than the other and how long does it take them to settle after the feed? The most important rule in making your own routine or adjusting one of the sample routines below is to make sure they are putting on weight and that their individual needs are being met. If you need any further help with creating routines please visit the Save Our Sleep website.

Sample routine for twin babies breastfeeding separately aged one week to two weeks and over 3 kg (6.6 lb)

Feed times for twin A	Feed times for twin B	Sleep times for twin A	Sleep times for twin B
6.35 am/7.25 am	7 am/7.45 am	7.50 am	8.15 am
9.35 am/10.25 am	10 am/10.45 am	11.05 am	11.30 am
12.35 pm/1.25 pm	1 pm/1.45 pm	2.05 pm	2.30 pm
3.35 pm/4.25 pm	4 pm/4.45 pm		
5.35 pm/6.25 pm	6 pm/6.30 pm	Bedtime 7 pm	Bedtime 7 pm
9.05 pm	9.30 pm		
2.25 am (at the latest)			

6.35 am

Wake baby **A** up and feed her for twenty minutes from your *right* breast. You will wake and feed her even if she last fed at 5.30 am, so she is always starting her day at the same time and on a full tummy. As you can see, I am allowing five minutes throughout for winding but this may take a little longer so adjust times if necessary.

7 am

Wake baby **B** up and feed him for twenty minutes from your *left* breast. You will wake and feed him even if he last fed at 5.30 am, so he is always starting his day at the same time and on a full tummy.

7.25 am

Put baby **A** back on your *right* breast and feed her for fifteen minutes.

7.45 am

Put baby **B** back on your *left* breast and feed him for fifteen minutes.

7.50 am

Take baby **B** off the *left* breast and swaddle baby **A**, put her in bed on her back awake and allow her to self-settle (see guide to self-settling starting on page 187). Burp baby **B** and put him back on *left* breast and continue feed.

8.15 am

Swaddle baby **B** and put him in bed on his back awake and allow him to self-settle.

9.35 am

Wake baby **A** up and feed her for twenty minutes from your *right* breast.

10 am

Wake baby **B** up and feed him for twenty minutes from your *left* breast.

10.25 am
Put baby **A** back on your *right* breast and feed her for fifteen minutes.

10.45 am
Put baby **B** back on your *left* breast and feed him for fifteen minutes.

11.05 am
Swaddle baby **A** and put her in bed on her back awake and allow her to self-settle.

11.30 am
Swaddle baby **B** and put him in bed on his back awake and allow him to self-settle.

12.35 pm
Wake baby **A** up and feed her for twenty minutes from your *right* breast.

1 pm
Wake baby **B** up and feed him for twenty minutes from your *left* breast.

1.25 pm
Put baby **A** back on your *right* breast and feed her for fifteen minutes.

1.45 pm
Put baby **B** back on your *left* breast and feed him for fifteen minutes.

2.05 pm
Swaddle baby **A** and put her in bed on her back awake and allow her to self-settle.

2.30 pm
Swaddle baby **B** and put him in bed on his back awake and allow him to self-settle.

3.35 pm
Wake baby **A** up and feed her for twenty minutes from your *right* breast.

4 pm
Wake baby **B** up and feed him for twenty minutes from your *left* breast.

4.25 pm
Put baby **A** back on your *right* breast and feed her for fifteen minutes.

4.45 pm
Put baby **B** back on your *left* breast and feed him for fifteen minutes. After this feed, put your babies down somewhere comfortable and safe, so if they feel like having a little nap they may. But don't put them in their beds as they may choose not to sleep. The best option would be to go for a walk at this time.

5.35 pm
Feed baby **A** for twenty minutes from your *right* breast.

6 pm
Feed baby **B** for twenty minutes from your *left* breast.

6.25 pm
Put baby **A** back on your *right* breast and feed her for five minutes.

6.32 pm
Put baby **B** back on your *left* breast and feed him for five minutes.

6.40 pm
Bath babies, or give top-to-toe wash. Some parents find it easier to bath their babies at another point earlier in the day. At this young age their bath does not have to be at the same time every day.

7 pm
Swaddle both babies and put them in bed on their backs awake and allow them to self-settle.

9.05 pm
Wake baby **A** up and feed her for twenty minutes from your *right* breast, then put her straight back in bed.

9.30 pm
Wake baby **B** up and feed him for twenty minutes from your *left* breast, then put him straight back in bed.

Night feeds
Set your alarm clock for 2.25 am every night, in case your babies have not woken for a feed: it is very important you don't go more than five hours without feeding at least one of your babies in week one. However, if one of your babies woke, for example, at 12.30 am and fed, then reset your alarm for 5.30 am. If you do need to wake one of your babies for a feed in the night, I advise you feed the smaller baby. But if either (or both) of them woke any time after 1.55 am and fed, reset your alarm for just before 7 am so you can get up and feed. During night feeds, try not to talk to your babies and keep the lights dim so they start to understand the difference between night and day.

Alternating your breasts
Every other day you are going to get baby **B** up first and feed him from the *right* breast all day. The first reason for this is the baby who gets woken first will have less sleep in the 24-hour period. If you alternate which baby gets woken first daily, you are less likely to have an overtired baby on your hands. The second reason I recommend

alternating each baby on one allocated breast to feed from in a 24-hour period, is this gives your breasts the equal opportunity to make breastmilk. If you feed baby **A** from the right breast, starting the feed at 7 am and then baby **A** again from the right breast at 10 am, there is a three-hour gap. However, if you feed baby **A** at 10 am from the left breast, which you last started feeding on at 7.25 am, that breast has only had a two hour and 35 minute break from feeding. I do not believe this to be a large enough gap to produce optimum breastmilk. I have also found this method to reduce mastitis in mothers breastfeeding more than one baby. You are still alternating between the breasts for each baby, which is recommended by most health professionals, but you are doing it every 24 hours, not at each feed. It's best to swap the allocated breast first thing in the morning, because this is usually when your breasts have had their longest break from feeding, so have had a chance to build up a good quantity of milk. It's also easier to remember to swap in the morning.

Sample routine for twin babies breastfeeding separately aged six to eight weeks

This is a sample routine for twin babies aged 42 to 56 days old. You will need to remember to feed one baby on one breast all day.

Feed times for twin A	Feed times for twin B	Sleep times for twin A	Sleep times for twin B
6.30 am	7 am	8 am	8.30 am
10.30 am	11 am	12 noon	12.30 pm
2.15 pm	2.45 pm	Nap 3.45 pm	Nap 4.15 pm
5.20 pm	5.50 pm	Bedtime 6.30 pm	Bedtime 7 pm
Dreamfeed 9.30 pm	Dreamfeed 10 pm		

6.30 am
Wake baby **A** up and feed her for 25 minutes from your *right* breast. You will wake and feed her even if she last fed at 5.30 am, so she is always starting her day at the same time on a full tummy.

7 am
Wake baby **B** up and feed him for 25 minutes from your *left* breast. You will wake and feed him even if he last fed at 5.30 am, so he is always starting his day at the same time and on a full tummy. After you have fed and winded baby **B** put baby **A** back on your *right* breast for a further fifteen minutes. Then put baby **B** back on the *left* breast for a further fifteen minutes.

8 am
Swaddle baby **A** and put her in bed on her back awake and allow her to self-settle (see guide to self-settling starting on page 187).

8.30 am
Swaddle baby **B** and put him in bed on his back awake and allow him to self-settle.

10.30 am
Wake baby **A** up and feed her for 25 minutes from your *right* breast.

11 am
Wake baby **B** up and feed him for 25 minutes from your *left* breast. After you have fed and winded baby **B** put baby **A** back on your *right* breast for a further 15 minutes. Then put baby **B** back on the *left* breast for a further 15 minutes.

12 noon
Swaddle baby **A** and put her in bed on her back awake and allow her to self-settle.

12.30 pm
Swaddle baby **B** and put him in bed on his back awake and allow him to self-settle.

2.15 pm
Wake baby **A** up and feed her for 25 minutes from your *right* breast.

2.45 pm
Wake baby **B** up and feed him for 25 minutes from your *left* breast. After you have fed and winded baby **B** put baby **A** back on your *right* breast for a further fifteen minutes. Then put baby **B** back on the *left* breast for a further fifteen minutes.

3.45 pm
Take your babies for a walk or out in the car to encourage them to sleep in places other than their beds.

4.45 pm
Wake your babies up if necessary. Sleeping past 4.45 pm could affect how well your babies settle at bedtime.

5 pm
Bath your babies, or give them a top-to-toe wash. Some parents find it easier to bath their babies every other night.

5.20 pm
Feed baby **A** for 25 minutes from your *right* breast.

5.50 pm
Feed baby **B** for 25 minutes from your *left* breast. After you have fed and winded baby **B** put baby **A** back on your *right* breast for a further eighteen minutes. Then put baby **B** back on the *left* breast for his further eighteen minutes.

6.40 pm
Swaddle baby **A** and put her in bed on her back awake and allow her to self-settle.

7 pm
Swaddle baby **B** and put him in bed on his back awake and allow him to self-settle.

9.30 pm
Give baby **A** a dreamfeed.

10 pm
Give baby **B** a dreamfeed.

Night feeds
Feed your babies when they wake during the night. During night feeds, try not to talk to your babies and keep the lights dim so they start to understand the difference between night and day.

Sample routine for twin babies bottle-feeding separately aged newborn to two weeks and over 3 kg (6.6 lb)

This is a sample routine for twin babies aged one to thirteen days old and over 3 kg (6.6 lb).

Feed times for twin A	Feed times for twin B	Sleep times for twin A	Sleep times for twin B
6.15 am	7 am	7.30 am	8.15 am
9.45 am	10.30 am	11 am	11.45 am
1.15 pm	2 pm	2.30 pm	3.15 pm
5.15 pm	6 pm	Bedtime 6.15 pm	Bedtime 7 pm
8.45 pm	9.30 pm		

Important: Always feed your baby until he is full – never give your baby a set amount.

6.15 am
Wake up baby **A** and feed her a bottle. You will wake and feed her even if she last fed at 5.30 am, so she is always starting her day at the same time and on a full tummy.

7 am
Wake up baby **B** and feed him a bottle. You will wake and feed him even if he last fed at 5.30 am, so he is always starting his day at the same time and on a full tummy.

7.30 am
Swaddle baby **A** and put her in bed on her back awake and allow her to self-settle (see guide to self-settling starting on page 187).

8.15 am
Swaddle baby **B** and put him in bed on his back awake and allow him to self-settle.

9.45 am
Wake up baby **A** and feed her a bottle.

10.30 am
Wake up baby **B** and feed him a bottle.

11 am
Swaddle baby **A** and put her in bed on her back awake and allow her to self-settle.

11.45 am
Swaddle baby **B** and put him in bed on his back awake and allow him to self-settle.

1.15 pm
Wake up baby **A** and feed her a bottle.

2 pm
Wake up baby **B** and feed him a bottle.

2.30 pm
Swaddle baby **A** and put her in bed on her back awake and allow her to self-settle.

3.15 pm
Swaddle baby **B** and put him in bed on his back awake and allow him to self-settle.

4.45 pm
Wake up baby **A** and bath her, or give a top-to-toe wash. Even if you choose not to bath your baby every night, you will still need to get her up at this time so she does not have too much sleep in the day.

5.15 pm
Feed baby **A** a bottle.

5.30 pm
Wake baby **B** up and, if you have help, bath him or give a top-to-toe wash. If you do not have help, allow this baby to sit in a bouncy chair or lie under a play gym until you have finished baby **A**'s feed (you could bath baby **B** before the 9.30 pm feed).

6 pm
Feed baby **B** a bottle.

6.15 pm
Interrupt baby **B**'s feed and swaddle baby **A** and put her in bed on her back awake and allow her to self-settle.

7 pm
Swaddle baby **B** and put him in bed on his back awake and allow him to self-settle.

8.45 pm
Wake up baby **A** and feed her a bottle.

9.30 pm
Wake up baby **B** and feed him a bottle.

Night feeds

Until your babies have regained their birth weight and are over 3 kg (6.6 lb), they should not be allowed to sleep longer than six hours at night without a feed. Set your alarm for 3.30 am every night in case your babies have not woken of their own accord. If this happens, feed your smaller baby first, then wake the next baby. However, if twin **B** woke at 11.30 pm and fed, for example, then reset the alarm clock for twin **B** for 5.30 am. If he woke any time after 1 am and fed, however, reset your alarm for just before 7.00 am, so you can get up and start feeding. During night feeds, try not to talk to your babies and keep the lights dim so they start to understand the difference between night and day. If your babies have regained their birth weight and are also over 3 kg (6.6 lb), you may allow them to sleep at night until they wake looking for a feed.

Sample routine for twin babies bottle-feeding separately aged six to eight weeks

This is a sample routine for twin babies aged 42 to 56 days old.

Feed times for twin A	Feed times for twin B	Sleep times for twin A	Sleep times for twin B
6.30 am	7 am	8 am	8.30 am
10.30 am	11 am	12 noon	12.30 pm
2.30 pm	3 pm	Nap 4 pm	Nap 4.30 pm
5.50 pm	6.20 pm	Bedtime 6.30 pm	Bedtime 7 pm
Dreamfeed 9.30 pm	Dreamfeed 10 pm		

6.30 am

Wake up baby **A** and feed her a bottle. You will wake and feed her even if she last fed at 5.30 am, so she is always starting her day at the same time and on a full tummy.

7 am
Wake up baby **B** and feed him a bottle. You will wake and feed him even if he last fed at 5.30 am, so he is always starting his day at the same time and on a full tummy.

8 am
Swaddle baby **A** and put her in bed on her back awake and allow her to self-settle (see guide to self-settling starting on page 187).

8.30 am
Swaddle baby **B** and put him in bed on his back awake and allow him to self-settle.

10.30 am
Wake up baby **A** and feed her a bottle.

11 am
Wake up baby **B** and feed him a bottle.

12 noon
Swaddle baby **A** and put her in bed on her back awake and allow her to self-settle.

12.30 pm
Swaddle baby **B** and put him in bed on his back awake and allow him to self-settle.

2.30 pm
Wake up baby **A** and feed her a bottle.

3 pm
Wake up baby **B** and feed him a bottle.

4 pm
Take your babies for a walk or out in the car to encourage them to have a nap in places other than their beds.

5.15 pm
Make sure both babies are awake from their naps.

5.20 pm
Bath your babies, or give top-to-toe wash.

5.50 pm
Feed baby **A** a bottle.

6.20 pm
Feed baby **B** a bottle.

6.30 pm
Swaddle baby **A** and put her in bed on her back awake and allow her to self-settle.

7 pm
Swaddle baby **B** and put him in bed on his back awake and allow him to self-settle.

9.30 pm
Give baby **A** a dreamfeed.

10 pm
Give baby **B** a dreamfeed.

Night feeds
Feed your babies when they wake during the night. During night feeds, try not to talk to your babies and keep the lights dim so they start to understand the difference between night and day.

TWIN TIPS

The first few months with a new baby can be very hard emotionally and physically, but for parents of more than one baby it is even harder. Juggling the care of two or more newborns is a round-the-clock job, with sleep deprivation adding to the physical strain and postpartum hormonal swings heightening emotions. Even experienced parents can stumble when their babies are born. Here are a few tips to help you get through the first months a little more easily.

Supplies

With more than one baby, supplies are consumed at a rapid rate. Stock up on the things you'll use most: nappies, wipes, cottonwool, bottles, teats and formula. An ample supply of bedding and baby clothes is a must; try to borrow some pre-loved spares from family and friends as you won't always have time to wash and dry everything. Keep any new items in their original packaging and hold on to receipts so you can easily return anything not used – you'll be amazed at how quickly your babies will grow out of clothes and nappies.

Napping

It may sound basic, but this advice is echoed repeatedly by parents of multiples. It's tempting to use the quiet time while your babies are sleeping to run around the house cleaning up, but you really need to rest yourself. You should try to have a nap at least once when your babies are asleep.

Prams and pushchairs

One of the trickiest aspects of managing multiples is the logistics of getting out and about, but be aware – if you don't get out you will slowly feel as if you are going crazy! A good pram or pushchair makes it much easier. Some parents prefer a tandem (front/back) style for manoeuvrability in tight spaces, while others find that a side-by-side model is more comfortable for their babies. Specialised ones are available for triplets and quads.

Confusing the babies

The more tired you get parenting twins or more, the harder it is to remember who fed or slept when. Setting up an organised system for keeping things straight will ensure that everyone's needs are met. Make a chart to track feeding times and amounts, nappy changes, medication and other important information. Or you might like to purchase the

Save Our Sleep *My Very First Diary*, which has customised charts already drawn up for the first twelve months of your baby's life. Please contact the Save Our Sleep team through the website for a twins' discount.

Take any help offered

People love new babies, and they genuinely want to help. Take advantage of every offer. Let your eager helpers take care of meals, errands, care of other siblings, housework, looking after the garden, walking the dog, laundry, shopping and all the details of life so that you can focus on you and your babies.

Take time out for yourselves

Even though your identities have changed to encompass your new roles as parents of multiples, you can't afford to neglect your old selves. It's important to take time out every once in a while to focus on yourselves. Take advantage of a helpful relative or friend, so you and your partner can have a break, even if you only go out for a coffee. Take it in turns in the day to give each other a break too, even if it's just to take a long bath. It is so important to have a few minutes a week to yourselves.

Join a twins' group

Meeting other parents of twins, triplets or more can be extremely reassuring and rewarding. Not only will they show you that life with multiples is doable, they can give you solid advice on just how to do it. It's crucial to establish a network of friends who have shared or are sharing the same experiences.

They will grow up

No matter how hard it may seem now, it will get better. Your babies will grow up and leave home one day, so the most important tip is to enjoy them while you can.

Tips:

- If your baby has to spend time in a special care nursery, it may be a good idea to take a room thermometer into the nursery a couple of days before you leave and find out exactly what temperature the nursery is. Then you can have the room your baby is going to sleep in at home the same temperature. Note what bedding the midwives use for him in the hospital and use the same amount at home.

- Remember most babies who have spent time in hospital will have never slept in complete silence or darkness. Try keeping a dim light on for the first few nights at home and slowly wean your baby off it.

COMMON QUESTIONS

My seven-month-old twin girls have started waking at night and are trying to wake each other up. What should I do? I wouldn't be too worried as I am sure it is a phase your babies will pass through with little fuss if you don't interfere and try to help them back to sleep. Your babies have more chance of getting back to sleep if you don't go into their room and try to help them. This will further stimulate and wake them up as well as creating a habit that might be hard to break.

I am expecting twins and am confused about feeding them. Will giving both formula and breastmilk harm them? It is perfectly safe to give your babies both breastmilk and formula – you do not mix the two in the same bottle but you can give both at one feed. Breastmilk is the best food for your babies but a mixture is better than no breastmilk at all and the more breastmilk you can give your babies, the cheaper the cost of having two will be!

My babies are two weeks old and one of the girls seems to get hungrier sooner than the second baby. Can I still follow your routines? I often see one twin bigger, stronger, able to take more at a feed and be satisfied longer than the other. So in the first few weeks, it can be hard to try to follow a routine where you are feeding both babies at the same time. I suggest feeding the baby who does not seem able to last between feeds for a longer period of time than the satisfied baby. This may mean giving her a break for a few minutes until she is ready to take a bit more.

I have four-month-old twins who are bottle-fed. How do I follow your routines? When following my routines with twins who are bottle-fed you need to follow the same routine that you would for one baby. If you are feeding your babies at the same time you use the normal routines stated on page 98 through to 110. If you are feeding your babies 30 to 45 minutes apart you adjust the routine slightly as shown in the sample routine on page 162.

9

SOLVING SLEEP PROBLEMS

Prevention is the best way to avoid sleep problems from occurring. If your baby is younger than eight weeks, establishing a good, proven routine and teaching her to self-settle will stop most sleep problems before they start. Even with a good routine, however, things can change overnight, causing unsettled sleep patterns in your household. In this chapter I will talk about the most common sleep problems I come across and how to solve them.

SLEEP DIARIES

It is a good idea to have a sleep diary to fill in before you start trying to change your baby or toddler's sleep habits. It is amazing how quickly you will forget how bad things were, and having this diary will help you (especially if at any point you feel like giving up). Then, once you start trying to correct sleep habits, note all you can in the diary.

The diary can be any old pad or notebook, and you could mark columns to put in information as follows:

- What time did your baby or toddler wake in the morning?

- What time did you put her down for each sleep?

- How long did your baby or toddler take to go to sleep?

- What time did she wake up?

- What time did you put your baby or toddler down for the night?

- How long did she take to go to sleep for the night?

- What time did your baby or toddler wake during the night?

- How long did she take to resettle?

- At the end of each 24-hour period, how many hours of sleep were achieved in total?

- At the end of each 24-hour period, how long did it take your baby or toddler to settle once put in bed in total?

Alternatively, you could purchase the Save Our Sleep *My Very First Diary*, which comes with ready-made charts allowing you to record everything about your baby's day. As you work through your sleep problem, you should look back over your diary to see the improvements you have made. This will keep your mind clear and your motivation high.

> **Tip:** Fill your neighbours in on the fact that they may hear some protests (see Zane's story below).

TRIGGERS FOR SLEEP PROBLEMS

Overtiredness
Overtiredness is a very common problem in babies and it surprises me how often it goes undiagnosed. When an adult is tired she tends to slow down, but when a baby or toddler gets tired they speed up and become hyperactive.

There are a few signals to look for in an overtired baby. Often a young baby of two to twelve weeks who is overtired will cry for long periods at night between 6 pm and midnight, and this is frequently mistaken for colic. A baby older than four weeks may start to refuse feeds or fall asleep when feeding. Furthermore, an overtired baby will do anything to stay awake, even refusing feeds. I have also come across many babies who start to feed normally but then suddenly begin screaming about ten minutes into a feed. On closer observation they are actually starting to relax and fall asleep at this point, but the stop-feeding and start-screaming behaviour is very similar to how a baby suffering from reflux would react, so an overtired baby is often misdiagnosed.

An overtired baby of about six months and older will fight you every time you put them in a situation where they might accidentally fall asleep, such as a car seat or pram. A tired adult lies down in bed and finds it easy to go to sleep, but the more tired a baby or toddler is, the longer they can fight the sleep and yell at you. When parents contact me about difficulties taking their baby or toddler out in a pram or car, in just about all cases the behaviour is brought on by overtiredness.

Zane's story:

When I met Zane he was fourteen months old and so overtired that he found normal, day-to-day life very difficult. Every time his parents took him out, he would scream so loudly that it came to the point where they just didn't go out unless they really had to. Their trips to the park or to see friends and family had become few and far between because Zane would not put up with being confined for more than five minutes without screams of protest starting. They had tried everything to calm him down but nothing seemed to help.

From the first chat on the phone with Zane's parents, I had a strong idea of exactly what was happening. When his parents put him in the car or pushchair he would be fine initially, but after five or ten minutes his eyes would start to get heavy as the car or pushchair gently lulled him towards sleep. However, as soon as Zane realised he was falling asleep, the screaming would start.

Zane's parents would then proceed as fast as they could to their destination to get him out of his pushchair or car seat. Sometimes they would even stop the car if the screaming became unbearable. What they had never considered was that responding to Zane's protests was actually teaching him to scream if he wanted to get out of the car or pushchair. In his rapidly developing little mind, he decided they had stopped and released him because he had protested long and loudly enough, not because they had reached the end of their journey.

In a lot of cases where a baby is fighting off the advent of sleep, the solution has been as simple as me jumping in the car with the parents and driving around for as long as necessary until the baby falls asleep. Alternatively, we will walk around a shopping centre with a screaming baby, trying our best to ignore the stares from disapproving shoppers.

Zane's case was a little different. We needed to sort out the whole picture, not just one single contributing factor within it. As is the case with most babies, Zane was fine in the car or pushchair up until about six months of age. This is the age at which a lot of sleep problems start to appear as, at six months, a baby who is aided to sleep (with a dummy, feed, rocking or patting) and then sleeps all night will generally start to wake again during the night due to newly developing night-time sleep cycles.

Zane's mum had been putting him to bed after he fell asleep with a bottle at about seven o'clock each evening. She would very carefully place him in his cot, praying he would stay there all night, but he seemed to be able to sense when she got to bed herself and would spring to life. He would then stand in his cot and shout for her to come and get him. Sleep deprivation over a period of time meant she found it easier at this point to just take him into her bed for the long night ahead. Zane would get a bottle every two hours but only take about 10 ml (0.3 oz) – this seemed easier to cope with than the screaming.

Since six months of age, Zane had never fallen asleep alone or without a bottle. Under such circumstances, he had probably never really entered into a deep sleep either. My experience is that babies who use

175

aids to get to sleep don't sleep as deeply or consistently as babies who put themselves to sleep. This in turn means they cannot drift from one sleep cycle to the next without fuss. So, in Zane's case, we had to solve his sleep problems first – only then would his resistance to a car seat or pushchair improve. Once the night-time sleeping was resolved we started taking him out during his day sleep times to get him used to being in a pushchair or car seat and his protests lasted no more than three minutes before he was sound asleep.

Here are a few things to keep in mind if you decide to tackle your baby's resistance to travelling in cars and pushchairs:

- Get a friend to go with you on walks and drives; support is a parent's best friend.

- Remember that it will get easier and shorter each time you win, so don't give in to the screams.

- Always stay calm, cool and confident – you are doing the right thing.

- Think of all the fun trips you can have once the battle is won!

- Don't make eye contact during screaming episodes as this will encourage the protest to continue.

- Always make sure your baby or toddler is safely strapped into her seat.

Catnapping

I define catnapping as daytime sleeps that are shorter than 40 minutes. The first time catnapping becomes a problem is when your baby starts to sleep in daytime sleep cycles (the process of drifting between light and deep sleep). An adult changes sleep cycle every 90 minutes but in babies it can be as short as twenty minutes. Daytime sleep cycles usually start when your baby is 6 kg (13.2 lb) or around eight weeks old. Most parents who contact me with concerns about catnapping do so when their babies are between eight and 25 weeks old. It is generally accepted that babies in this age range should have two daytime sleeps of between 80 and 120 minutes in duration, and possibly another shorter nap as well.

Many parents find that when they finally get their baby to sleep, they wake after twenty to 40 minutes and start crying. This is not because the baby has had enough sleep and is ready to get up but because she has not learned to resettle from one sleep cycle to the next. As babies become more aware of their environment and its distractions, it is the parents' responsibility to teach their baby to move from one sleep cycle to the next as quickly and as quietly as possible.

Babies will never develop the skill to resettle themselves until they have learned to put themselves to sleep in the first place. If a baby is unable to resettle herself she will invariably start to cry, as that is her only method of communication. This doesn't usually mean that something is seriously wrong. However, in my experience, 95 per cent of babies who only manage short catnaps, without stringing together multiple sleep cycles, will spend most of the day grumpy and irritable through lack of sleep. This is irrespective of how well they sleep at night.

There are a few reasons I have found for a baby to catnap. The first and most common reason is the baby has always been aided to sleep, that is, given a dummy to suck on or fed, rocked or shushed to sleep by a parent. The second reason I have found babies to catnap is hunger. The hunger can be caused by snack feeding or can be brought on from dummy use, as I believe the sucking reflex causes the baby's digestive system to work too fast. The hunger can also be because your baby is not being offered enough milk or is no longer satisfied on milk alone and is ready to start on solids foods. If your baby is four months or older you should introduce solids, following my weaning advice on page 116. Your baby may also be cold. Often if she is not dressed correctly or covered with enough layers she will be too cold to resettle when she wakes after a sleep cycle. For further information please see the cold at sleep time section on page 183.

There are a few ways you can determine why your baby is catnapping and what you can do to solve this problem. The first and most important step is to follow the 24-hour routine for your baby's age group. It is very important to only put her to bed at the sleep times recommended in the routines. One of the reasons she could be catnapping is because you are putting her to bed at the first sign of tiredness. Often, however, when your baby first starts to show signs of tiredness, she will only be tired enough to nap and not tired enough to sleep.

I recommend keeping your baby awake until the times specified in the routines to ensure she will be tired enough to sleep well. This can sometimes be difficult in the first few days of establishing a routine or moving from one routine to the next. If you find it difficult to keep your baby awake, you can try a little bath or a walk around the garden or some nappy-free play to keep her stimulated for the extra amount of time necessary.

If your baby wakes after 40 minutes or less, the best thing to do is to get her up and praise her going to sleep in the first place. If your baby is under sixteen weeks old, keep her wrapped and sit in a chair with her on your chest and pat her back to the rhythm of your heartbeat to encourage more sleep in the allocated time. If your baby is over sixteen weeks old, you could try popping her in the pram and going for a walk or drive in the car to encourage more sleep. If your baby goes back to sleep happily, you can assume that she just needed to learn to resettle, and I would suggest you follow my self-settling guidelines later in this chapter. I would also suggest that you look at your baby's bedding as resettling while lying on you or in the pram or car can indicate that she is cold. Please read my safe bedding guide available on the Save Our Sleep website for the most up-to-date bedding guidelines.

If your baby continually squirms and cries out when you are putting her down to sleep, hunger might be causing the catnapping and you may need to look at feeding her more milk. This can involve making sure you always offer both breasts, and possibly a top-up of expressed breastmilk in a bottle straight after a breastfeed, or making sure you offer more formula if she drains her bottle. If your baby is over sixteen weeks old it may be that milk alone is no longer satisfying her and you should think about introducing solids – see my weaning advice from page 116 onwards. If your baby is happy to lie awake when you get her up and does not either go back to sleep or cry for food, you may need to look at giving her an extra fifteen minutes of awake time before her sleep or moving her to the next routine.

If you feel your baby's catnapping problem could be the result of her not knowing how to self-settle, I suggest you follow the self-settling guides for her age later in this chapter.

Amy's story

Amy was fifteen weeks old and her parents had employed the help of two different sleep nannies when I met her but neither had been able to help. After talking to parents Gail and Enan, I discovered Amy's routine was very similar to mine and she was put to bed with no sleep aids, only her comforter, so these factors weren't the issue. So where was the problem? It turned out Amy had not been able to self-settle at all before the nannies had visited. After sleep school, when Gail or Enan put Amy in bed and asked her to go to sleep, she would usually take anything from ten minutes to one hour and twenty minutes to settle, always waking again after just one sleep cycle. Gail had been told by both nannies to then try to resettle Amy until her next feed was due.

Unfortunately, neither Gail nor Enan had ever managed to resettle Amy and I explained that I felt the problem stemmed from these failed attempts. I suggested putting Amy in her cot, asking her to go to sleep and getting her up when she next woke, no matter how little sleep Amy had had. Then, when the next sleep was due, the settling time should reduce to about half, and again for each subsequent sleep. This would happen because they would be giving Amy a clear message that she will get up after she has had a sleep. If they continued to ask Amy to resettle and then, after maybe 40 minutes of a resettling challenge, they go in and pick her up, all they are doing is teaching Amy that if she fights sleep they will eventually come in and get her. This was why the 'going to sleep' time was not getting any shorter. I explained that once Amy went to sleep with no protesting, she would resettle naturally and sleep longer.

The next day Gail put Amy to bed at 9 am and it took Amy until 9.40 am to get to sleep. Then, like clockwork Amy woke at 10.20 am and Gail got her up. Gail was concerned about how to keep Amy up until 1 pm but she managed it. At the 1 pm sleep it took Amy only eighteen minutes to get to sleep but again Amy was up after 40 minutes. That night at 7 pm it only took Amy eight minutes to get to sleep.

On day two Amy took twelve minutes to get to sleep at 9 am but this meant that at 9.52 am Amy was awake. Now Gail was really concerned about how she was going to keep Amy up until 1 pm as because Amy had settled faster, she now had longer to stay awake before the next sleep. To Gail, the problem looked worse. It was too hot outside for a walk so we decided to put Amy in the baby swing where she could nap before her next feed if she wanted to.

At 1 pm Amy went down without a noise and Gail had to wake her at 3 pm for her breastfeed. Gail was convinced this was only because Amy was so exhausted after being up for over three hours, but the next day and every day since Amy has not catnapped.

> **Tip:** Before trying to resolve your baby's catnapping issues please read the information about catnapping on page 176.

EARLY RISING

I believe that all babies are capable of sleeping in until 7 am, and there is no such thing as an 'early riser'. If you are finding that your baby settles and sleeps well at 7 pm only to wake up at 5 am every morning ready to start the day, take a look at some of the common causes I have found for early rising.

The bedtime ritual

If the last milk feed or story is too close to bedtime your baby could be using this as a sleep aid and be going to bed already sleepy. Then, when your baby wakes at 5 am, she is looking for the same aid to help her back to sleep. Often just changing the bedtime ritual and making sure the last twenty minutes before bed is taken up with stimulating play will help her sleep until 7 am.

For more information, check out the example bedtime ritual on page 143.

Is your baby warm enough to sleep all night?

A big contributing factor to babies and toddlers not sleeping through the night is temperature. The baby's room should be heated to 20°C. I have often found that just by adding an extra layer or two of cotton or bamboo blankets to your baby's bed, along with dressing them appropriately , your baby will sleep in until 7 am. If you find it is too warm to add the extra layers at 7 pm, you can also try adding them after the dreamfeed or just before you go to bed for the night.

The time of the daytime sleep

It might be that your baby is having her daytime sleep too early in the day. The time a baby has her first sleep of the day will affect the time she wakes up the following day. So, if the warmth and the bedtime ritual are not issues, start to move the daytime sleep. If your baby is currently going to bed at 9 am for the first sleep of the day, try a 9.20 am bedtime. If she is going down at 9.50 am already, try a 10 am morning sleep. If you have a toddler, I suggest moving your toddler's day sleep back by twenty minutes every three days until you find a time that your baby is sleeping in until 7 am in the morning.

Too much daytime sleep

Some babies and toddlers need less daytime sleep than others, so you can also try cutting the amount of daytime sleep to see if this helps your baby sleep in until 7 am. An average amount of daytime sleep for babies under five months old is four hours and 45 minutes; for a baby aged five to seven months, the average is four hours and twenty minutes; a baby aged seven to nine months will usually sleep for four hours; and a baby aged nine to twelve months will sleep for an average of just three hours. Once a baby reaches twelve months old it is a little harder to give average times, but I would not let a baby of between twelve and eighteen months sleep longer than two hours and 30 minutes; a toddler of between eighteen months and two years longer than two hours and fifteen minutes; a toddler aged two years should sleep no longer than two hours; and a toddler aged three years no longer than an hour during the day.

Your baby's diet
Some babies rise early because all of their nutritional needs are not being met. In some cases, introducing meat or fish into the baby or toddler's diet stops the early rising. In other cases, certain types of baby food can cause early rising, I have also found custard of any variety, be it shop bought, homemade from custard powder or homemade from scratch, to be a problem, so it's worth looking into your baby's diet if she is rising early.

Changing the 7 pm bedtime
If none of the above works, what next? I suggest trying to move your baby's bedtime. I have in the past moved the bedtime to 6.30 pm – and bingo! – the baby or toddler sleeps until after 7 am. So if all else fails, try moving your baby's bedtime to 6.30 pm.

The morning sleep
It has been my experience over the years that the time a baby wakes up in the morning can be affected by the time you put her down for her first sleep of the day. I have not yet worked out why this is so, but I can tell you it does have an impact having tested this theory out on lots of babies and having always got the same results. This usually only applies to babies older than seven months. If you are following my routine and putting your baby of between seven and nine months down for her first sleep of the day at 9.20 am each morning but she is waking at 6.15 am or earlier from the night sleep instead of 7 am, try moving the 9.20 am sleep to 9.50 am. If your baby is over nine months, try moving the 9.50 am sleep to 10.15 am. Nine times out of ten this will then have her sleeping in each morning until 7 am.

Cold at sleep time

This is a topic which comes up frequently for me. I have spent the last four years mostly doing my home visits in Australia, but for ten years before that I was in the UK. The thing that surprises me most is the difference between how the two sides of the world dress their babies at night.

In the UK, parents put a lot more clothing on their babies at night, and the temperature of their homes is actually warmer than the night-time temperature of most of the homes I visit in Australia. The type of central heating used in the UK seems to keep the house at a more even temperature throughout the night in the winter. Also, in Australia during the summer, I have noticed babies get very cold if an air-conditioner is running.

I am not even sure if it is the warmth that babies like or if the extra layers make them feel cosier and more secure. But I do know that extra layers can stop babies from waking during day and night sleeps.

Rylen's story

Nine-month-old Rylen's parents were concerned about how restlessly he was sleeping at night and how early he was waking in the mornings. At the time, Rylen was on the sleep routine for his age and didn't have any settling problems.

Rylen would go to bed at 7 pm and get himself to sleep in a few minutes. But come midnight, he would start to move about the cot, banging his head and often getting his arms stuck between the cot bars. This unsettled sleep would go on all night until 5 am, when he would wake up and be unable to get back to sleep.

Rylen's parents, Claire and John, didn't mind starting their day at 5 am, but they were worried about his restless nights. So they asked me to come and visit to help Rylen sleep more soundly.

One of the first things I did when I arrived at their home was to look at where Rylen slept and what he wore to bed. I saw that his cot had cot bumpers on it and explained to Claire and John that the research

I had read about cot death states cot bumpers are not safe. There was also no bedding in Rylen's cot or around his room. Claire and John explained that they'd been told bedding was unsafe and to use a sleeping bag as a safe alternative to bedding. Since studies on cot death suggest that the safest way for a baby to sleep is on his back, I have always advised my clients to put their babies in a safe sleeping bag. However, I always recommend safe sleeping bags are used with bedding, not as an alternative.

Sleeping bags are a great piece of bedding and help keep babies warm at night, which in return will stop them rolling onto their tummies to warm up, and moving around their cot. They also stop babies kicking their bedding loose, which can become a safety issue all of its own, and they help babies to feel safe and secure – some babies even use them as a comforter when going to sleep.

I explained that although Claire and John were warned not to overheat Rylen (as it could be a factor contributing to cot death), it was vital to ensure their baby was not too cold as well. In my opinion, the consequences of a baby being cold at night can be just as dangerous as overheating him. A baby who is cold will roll to his tummy as soon as he is physically able. Once on his tummy he will sleep with his face buried in the mattress, trying to warm himself up. He will also, once able to, move all around the cot, often banging his head and getting his arms and legs stuck in the bars.

I explained that I believed the reason for Rylen's restless nights was that he was feeling cold. So that night we took the cot bumpers out of Rylen's cot and dressed him in a bodysuit, a babygro, a 2.5 tog sleeping bag, a sheet and four bamboo blankets, popping a fifth one on last thing before we all went to bed for the night. Rylen went to bed at 7 pm on the dot and, to his mum and dad's relief, he didn't move all night and slept until we woke him, just before 7 am.

I've observed very similar results with many babies and toddlers over the years. Through the winter months thousands of parents contact me about their babies who had been sleeping perfectly, but all of a sudden are waking at 4 am. Once advised to pop cotton or bamboo blankets on top of the sleeping bag these babies begin to sleep peacefully through the night again.

Your baby's room should be at a comfortable temperature all night. I suggest cooling a baby's room to 22°C in summer (if you are using air-conditioning), or warming it to 20°C in winter. If you do not have central heating, I suggest using an oil-filled column heater. A good way of keeping an eye on the temperature is to use a room thermometer.

In addition to your baby's room temperature, you can adjust his body temperature by adding or removing blankets. The reason I recommend using bamboo or cotton blankets along with a safe sleeping bag, and not normally using more than two layers of clothing, is because more than two layers under a sleeping bag can be a risk of its own. You might, for example, as advised by some sleeping bag manufacturers, add extra layers under your baby's sleeping bag. Then, when you go in to check your baby at night and discover she feels too hot, decide to not risk lifting her to remove the lower layers because you are scared to wake her. You and I would like to think we would put safety first, but it's important to remember that on some nights we might feel too tired to risk waking our sleeping baby.

On the other hand, if you find your baby is too cold without enough layers under her sleeping bag you might just grab the nearest thing – like a quilt or polyester blanket – and throw it over her. A safer approach is to have the correct safe bedding at hand and educate the people who are around your baby at sleep times about how to put your little one to bed safely.

When I refer to sleeping bags, I am talking about the safe products recommended on the Save Our Sleep website. In my opinion, these are the safest sleeping bags available and I have tested many different brands. Currently, the one I believe to be the safest is not easily available in the United Kingdom and Ireland but I hope this will change or an equal one will become available to you. As safety and the wellbeing of babies and children is my main concern, I have looked into other brands and keep an eye on new products that are just hitting the market. I can happily say none of them come near to the safety or quality of those on the website. In my years of working with sleeping bags I've seen zips and poppers that come off, necks and arm holes that are too big (allowing babies to fall into them and climb out) and sleeping bags with Velcro on them (allowing them to become attached to mattresses). I have experienced none of these problems with the safe sleeping bags I currently recommend.

Teething

Teething is the name given to the movement of your baby's teeth and it gets the blame for a lot of things during the first couple of years of her life. Many parents falsely believe that teething is the cause of the sudden onset of night-waking behaviour in a baby of around six months, but in most cases the real cause is the start of night-time sleep cycles.

I believe that if you put your baby to bed at 7 pm and she goes to sleep in her normal way but wakes again within the hour crying an emotional cry, teething could be to blame, but this is only if it is a one-off waking and not a habit. If this is the case I suggest you get your baby up and give her whatever you normally would for pain; a homeopathic rescue remedy for teething, some baby paracetamol or whatever you usually use for her. Then keep her up for twenty minutes before putting her back to bed. **Don't give your baby any new medications at night-time in case she has an allergic reaction.**

If your baby wakes more than an hour after going to sleep then I am less likely to believe that movement of teeth is causing the problem because sleep decreases blood pressure, which causes pain tolerance to increase. While you are awake your blood pressure gets higher which causes your pain tolerance to get lower; this is why you can go to bed with a headache and sleep well all night, then wake in the morning and think it has gone only to realise it is back about an hour later as your blood pressure rises.

Teething is also blamed for nappy rash and diarrhoea by a lot of parents. I too have seen first-hand a baby with nappy rash or diarrhoea one day and no symptoms but a new tooth the next; however, a medical connection between these events has never been found. I have also seen some babies repeatedly get an ear infection before they get a tooth but this is very rare and there is no evidence the two are connected either.

So please tread very carefully before going down the track of giving your baby reassuring cuddles and walks around the house based upon beliefs that teething causes night waking. These actions are often instead the start of an ongoing sleep problem.

TEACHING YOUR CHILD TO SETTLE

Self-settling guide for a baby who is not yet standing

At the recommended sleep time, swaddle your baby in a Doublewrap (if your baby is still at the swaddling stage) and put her in bed awake on her back without a dummy. Walk out of the room leaving the door halfway open so your baby can hear you. Allow her to protest (cry) for the amount of time you feel strong enough to leave her for (you will need to stay out for the recommended minimum time as per the table if you are going to successfully teach your baby to self-settle).

SAVE OUR SLEEP SELF-SETTLING GUIDE

Age	After putting your baby to bed, walk out of the room for a minimum time of:	When you decide you cannot listen to your baby's protest cry any longer, go in and try to settle her for the below time before taking a break	After your ten-minute break, put your baby back to bed and start again with the below minimum times
Newborn to 2 weeks	2 minutes	22 minutes	2 minutes
2 to 8 weeks	4 minutes	22 minutes	4 minutes
8 to 12 weeks	6 minutes	22 minutes	6 minutes
3 to 4 months	8 minutes	22 minutes	8 minutes
4 to 6 months	12 minutes	46 minutes	12 minutes

6 months until your baby is standing in her cot	18 minutes	46 minutes	18 minutes
Standing in the cot to 9 months	Lay your baby down 15 times and then walk out for a minimum of 18 minutes	46 minutes	Lay your baby down 15 times and then walk out for a minimum of 18 minutes
9 to 12 months	Lay your baby down 15 times and then walk out for a minimum of 20 minutes	Stay with your baby until she is asleep	n/a
12 months until in a bed	Lay your baby down 15 times and stay out until your baby is asleep	No help needed	n/a

When timing the recommended minimum time, only count continuous protesting: if there is a gap of five seconds or more you need to start timing again. The longer you are able to resist going in and helping your baby settle, the faster your baby will be able to learn the important skill of self-settling. When employing transitional sleeping tactics as recommended here, always time the period of crying as one minute may seem like ten to a parent listening to their baby protest.

It is important to remember that a protesting cry is normal and doesn't necessarily mean that something is seriously wrong. In teaching a baby to settle herself, inevitably there will be some protest cries. If you listen to your baby's cries, you will notice they become very high-pitched after a while. Most parents have never heard this pitch of crying before and they therefore give up, thinking there is a problem. However, when I am working with parents and their babies I note this as a turning point: we are winning and the baby will soon be asleep. This high-pitched crying is often described as 'peaking'.

If you are strong enough to not respond to these high-pitched yells, your baby will start to fall asleep. Also during this stage, there will be breaks in the baby's protests – these gaps will start to get longer and the shouting shorter until finally your baby is sound asleep. When you are sure your baby is asleep, wait a few minutes before going in to reposition or cover her up. Try not to reposition her too much as you may accidentally move her away from something she was comforting herself with before falling asleep.

Parents need to remember that the crying will be less frequent and shorter in duration as the baby develops the skills to settle herself. The challenge for parents is to resist the temptation to comfort their catnapping baby every time she cries.

When you can't handle the protesting and the minimum time is up for your baby's age (see chart starting on page 187), go back into her room. Try to avoid eye contact while you are settling her. Place your hand on your baby's tummy and gently pat or rub her. Alternatively, you can stroke her forehead, making sure she remains in the safe back-sleeping position. If your baby is younger than sixteen weeks old you can continue this settling process for 22 minutes. If she is over sixteen weeks old and not yet standing in the cot you can continue this settling process for 46 minutes. If after the required time your baby has still not settled you can get her up for a ten-minute break, but if you are still feeling strong, calm, confident and patient, keep up the settling techniques as the break is for your benefit, not your baby's. If you choose to take a break, begin the whole process again afterwards, starting with staying out for the minimum time. *Don't give up. You are going to win this encounter.* Once your baby is asleep stay in the room for an extra few minutes to ensure she is sound asleep.

It is normal that when your baby has settled to sleep she will wake again after just one sleep cycle. As frustrating as this may seem, during the day you need to get her up and praise her for going to sleep in the first place. You won the going-to-sleep challenge! Your baby will soon start to resettle and sleep longer but only after she has learnt the skill of self-settling. If you know she needs more sleep, go for a walk or a drive so she can perhaps have a nap before her next milk feed.

If your baby wakes during the night, feed her if she is still having night feeds and then settle her with the appropriate settling techniques for her age. If she is no longer having night feeds, do not go in to settle her until the minimum protest time has passed. But remember that your baby is more likely to get back to sleep if you stay out of her room – going in may wake her up further.

Self-settling guide for a baby who is standing to twelve months old

Many parents first contact me when their babies are around nine months old, and in most cases there is a similar theme to the calls. They will tell me that they had a good sleeper until about six months of age but their baby has started to frequently wake at night. These parents often believe that teething is the cause of this sudden onset of night-waking behaviour, as this is about the time that teeth start to come through for many babies. But in most cases the start of night-time sleep cycles is the actual cause. For the next three months, many parents spend the nights hoping the teething will go away and that their baby will resume her all-night sleeping routine again. However, by about nine months the waking is usually getting more frequent and baby is often starting to stand up in her cot.

Once I assess the parental behaviour and home environment, it often becomes clear that these babies have never learned to fall asleep without a sleep aid, such as being rocked, patted, fed or given a dummy. Before six months of age, this problem does not seem evident in night-time sleeping as in these early stages of development, if all other needs are satisfied, you can assist your baby towards slumber and she will comfortably sleep all night. But at about six months this changes because she starts to surface between sleep cycles during the night and is more aware of her surroundings, relationships and needs. So if your baby has been aided in going to sleep, she will start to wake at night looking for the same comfort in order to resettle.

In such circumstances, I explain to parents that we need to teach their baby the skill of self-settling. Personally, I disagree with controlled crying as a means of teaching babies the skill of self-settling or resettling. In my opinion, walking in and out is teasing your baby and only makes both you and your baby upset. I recommend what I call the 'lay-down approach', which shows your baby what you want her to do.

Tip: Make yourself a score chart allocating one point to your baby if you have to give up during the settling process or one point to yourself for a successful settle. You will surprise yourself – after a few days you'll be winning every time. And remember that good daytime sleep encourages good night-time sleep; the two complement each other.

If your baby stops crying almost as soon as you pick her up, there is probably not much wrong with her. If you are still not sure, try picking her up again when she cries and see what happens. If she stops again you can be reassured that it can't be too serious.

I recommend you make a mental note to lower your baby's cot to its lowest setting at six months. I all too often hear of babies going from sitting to standing in their cot for the first time and then falling out. If you are going to try and solve a sleep problem which involves leaving your baby protesting in her cot then it is very important the cot is lowered.

Important note: If you have previously used my routines and your baby was self-settling and sleeping well, you do not need to use the lay-down approach. Your baby will already know what you expect of her when you put her in the cot. I often see babies who have happily been on a routine for months suddenly start to stand in their cots when they have learned this new skill. What I recommend you do is to totally ignore this behaviour. Put your baby to bed in the normal way and leave the room. If she stands up you need to ignore her and leave her. She will know that you expect her to lie down and go to sleep and the less attention you give her the quicker she will stop standing. However, if you are unsure that you have ever taught your baby to self-settle then I recommend you try the following approach.

The lay-down approach

I use this technique for babies who have started to stand in their cot until they are twelve months old because I am never sure if they really know what you want them to do when put in their cot. Using this 'lay-down' technique gives babies in this age group a clear message that you would like them to lie down and go to sleep.

The first step is to adhere as closely as possible to a proven 24-hour routine suitable for the age of your baby. Start a few days before by telling your baby what you are planning to do, letting her know in a firm but soothing voice that you will be putting her to bed awake and without the usual assistance and that, irrespective of how much protesting goes on, you will not be getting her up until she has had a good sleep. This may be bolstering your resolve as much as helping your baby, but I also believe parents should never underestimate their ability to communicate with their babies.

The thing I like about this method is that your baby actually shouts rather than cries. It may initially sound like crying to you, but in fact your baby is shouting for you to pick her up. She is not crying out in pain or discomfort, so you must be strong and determined if you are to win this challenge – and you will.

At this point it is important to remember that a noisy baby doesn't necessarily mean that something is seriously wrong. In teaching a baby to settle there will inevitably be some protests, but parents must accept that these will be less frequent and shorter in duration as your baby develops the skills she needs to settle to sleep. The challenge for parents is to learn to read the sounds made by their baby and to resist the temptation to comfort them every time they protest.

Take your baby into her cot, emphasise that it is bedtime and that you will be there again when she has had a sleep. It is a good idea at this point to have a bedtime ritual that you do at each sleep: it could be saying goodnight to the cars parked outside in the street and shutting the curtains, or you could simply say goodnight to a few favourite soft toys. Then I suggest you give your baby her sleep comforter and start the lay-down approach.

Lay your baby down in her cot on her back. Stand back a little and watch. If she has taught herself to stand up, she will do so at this stage. When she does stand up, gently lay her down again to give a clear message about what you want her to do. Each time she stands up you will respond by laying her back down again. Do this fifteen times and then walk out of the room. At this point there will be loud protests but don't worry, you are going to win this challenge and she will fall asleep.

Stay out of the room for the minimum time I have recommended for your baby's age (see self-settling guide, starting on page 187). Make sure you time this as five minutes can seem like twenty when listening to your baby protest. When the minimum time is reached and if you are feeling strong enough to listen to a bit more protesting, stay out. Your baby will learn to self-settle much faster if you can stay out. But if you feel you have to go in to her, enter and lay her down again. Now you are going to stay with her until she is asleep.

This time you will need to continue to lay your baby down until she is asleep. This could be in excess of 40 times (trust me, this will work). When you notice she taking longer to stand up I recommend you put your hand on your baby's back or tummy and say 'good girl' just the once. If she is trying to stand up, don't resist – take your hand away and continue to lay her down as before. But if your baby is staying down, keep your hand on her back or tummy as a reward. Only leave your hand there for a minute and then take it away again. Don't give up if she stands up again, just continue with the lay-down technique until she starts to stay down, then use your hand as a comfort again. Stay with your baby until she is asleep. Your presence may seem like an aid at this point, but after a few self-settling attempts she will start to fall asleep without you there.

This first challenge is always the longest and hardest. Strong, healthy babies can protest for what seems to be an interminably long time. You can expect the second challenge to be about half the time, and the third half again. In my experience, on the fourth attempt, the baby usually goes down with little or no fuss. But just as you believe you are getting somewhere because your baby went down for her last sleep with little fuss, she will give you the biggest challenge ever. This happens on about day three – and you will be able to win this because you are expecting it. Once you get past this hurdle, your sleep problems will be solved. It is as if all the babies I have worked with give one last, big attempt to win and be in charge of their parents, but after failing they decide to settle with no fuss from then on.

This method must be continued each night and day until your baby stops getting up. It may seem tedious, but it is better than being woken every night for the next five years or more! It is also important that you take your hand off before your baby falls asleep or your hand will become a sleep aid and the goal of self-settling will not be reached. Each time you complete this ritual, move further away when you remove your hand – if your baby stands up again, you know what to do. Your aim is to get further away each night so she starts to fall asleep alone.

I recommend that if your baby wakes after just one sleep cycle during the day and you know she needs more sleep, get her up. Praise her for going to sleep in the first place and then you could go for a walk or a drive to try to encourage more sleep in the recommended sleep time. After a few days of sticking to the routine, your catnapping baby should be resettling herself. But at night-time you will ask her to resettle. It is best to try not to go in and help her to resettle as by going in you will just be waking her up further and she will find it even harder to go back to sleep. So try not to go in, or try to stay out for at least my minimum time for your child's age, but if you feel at any point you have to go in, then do the lay-down approach and stay with your baby until she is asleep.

> **Tips:**
>
> - Always leave the side of the cot up. Never adjust the side of the cot up or down when your baby is in it as this will create the feeling that the cot is a boundary between yourself and your baby.
>
> - Plan to start the lay-down approach on a night when you and your partner can afford to miss a little sleep – Friday, for example.
>
> - Always remain calm, confident and consistent in your approach. Babies thrive on confident parents.

Important note: If you have previously used my routines and your baby was self-settling and sleeping well, you do not need to use the lay-down approach. Your baby will already know what you expect of her when you put her in the cot. I often see babies who have happily been on a routine for months suddenly start to stand in their cots when they have learned this new skill. What I recommend you do is to totally ignore this behaviour. Put your baby to bed in the normal way and leave the room. If she stands up you need to ignore her and leave her. She will know that you expect her to lie down and go to sleep and the less attention you give her the quicker she will stop standing. However, if you are unsure that you have ever taught your baby to self-settle then I recommend you try the following approach.

Night-waking in babies over twelve months

Many parents contact me at the one-year mark, totally frustrated by their babies' consistent waking during the night and needing feeding, dummy replacement or rocking to go back to sleep. Once again, in most of these cases I find that the babies have never learned to self-settle in the first place, so they do not have the skills to resettle when they wake during the night.

No adult, child or baby will ever sleep through the entire night without waking, but in childhood we develop the ability to get back to sleep with little or no fuss. It is a parent's responsibility to ensure these skills are taught to babies as early as possible.

Having worked with hundreds of babies over the years, it is my opinion that when they wake during the night they are looking for the last thing they were thinking of when they initially fell asleep. When I ask parents if they put their baby down awake they generally believe they do. But what many don't realise is that while their baby may look like she is awake, she has already begun reaching that heavy-eyed, falling-asleep stage while feeding, sucking on a dummy or being rocked. In reality, she has been aided into slumber, so when she wakes during the night she wants that same help to get back to sleep. Unfortunately, by the time the parents give in to the crying baby and feed, rock or put the dummy back in, some babies are fully awake thus making resettling much harder.

Where do we go from here?

The way I see it, you have three relatively straightforward options:

1 Continue what you have been doing and hope that some day the problem will go away. This is not recommended for the long-term sanity of babies and their parents!

2 Utilise a controlled-crying technique, a method that many books and baby health professionals recommend. This sometimes works, but it can be traumatising for babies and parents alike and I don't recommend this technique for babies of any age. Babies get very upset and confused when their parents continually come in and out, because the rules are difficult to learn. Effectively you are teasing your baby and often just teaching her to cry for longer periods.

3 Then there is what is called the 'deep-end approach', which is what I recommend for most parents with babies over one year of age. As opposed to walking in slowly from the shallow end of the pool, I think it is better to just jump straight into the deep end. I find this method gets rapid results, with baby and family becoming happier and more rested.

The deep-end approach

The deep-end approach is almost the same as my lay-down approach. Start in the same way by telling your toddler in the days leading up to the changes what is going to happen. Explain in a firm but soothing voice that you will be putting her to bed awake and that no matter how much standing and shouting she does, you will not be getting her out of bed until she has had a sleep. Your baby will understand a lot more than you think.

With this approach your toddler will actually be having a temper tantrum about not wanting to go to bed rather than crying emotionally, as is the case with controlled crying.

How it works

Take your baby into her bed and tell her it's time to go to sleep. Say your normal goodnights and lay her in bed, then stay and wait for her to fully stand up. When she stands you will lay her down again carefully, taking care not to be too rough (this gives her a clear message as to what you want her to do). Each time she stands up, you will lay her down again. She will be protesting but don't worry, you are going to win the going-to-sleep encounter! After you have laid her down ten times, walk out of the room.

This is when the protests will really begin as your baby starts to shout for you to come back in. After about twenty minutes – although it could be considerably longer if she has learnt to cry until you eventually come in – she will stop calling for you. Trust me on this. Eventually your baby will calm down for a second or two. Then she will realise she is falling asleep and at this point the shouting will change in tone to sound more desperate, like she has been stung by a bee, as your baby becomes cross with herself for giving in. Most parents have never heard this tone of shouting before and they therefore give up, thinking there is a problem. But when I am working with parents and their babies I note this as a turning point. I know we are winning!

This secondary shouting stage generally lasts about the same time as the first shouting stage before a third and final stage begins. This is when the baby will start to fall asleep. Don't worry if at this point she is standing or sitting in her bed as she will lie down before reaching deep sleep. During this stage there will be breaks in the baby's protests and these gaps will start to get longer and the shouting shorter until finally she is sound asleep. When you are sure your baby is asleep, wait six minutes before going in to reposition or cover her up. Try not to reposition her too much as you may accidentally move her away from something she was comforting herself with before falling asleep.

This first challenge is always the longest and hardest. Strong, healthy babies can protest for what seems to be an interminably long time. You can expect the second challenge to be about half the time, and the third half again. In my experience, on the fourth attempt, your baby usually goes down with little or no fuss.

I recommend that if your baby wakes after just one sleep cycle during the day and you know she needs more sleep, get her up. Praise her for going to sleep in the first place and then you could go for a walk or a drive to try to encourage more sleep in the recommended sleep time. After a few days of sticking to the routine and the deep-end approach, her will start to go to sleep with little or no fuss. This is when your baby will sleep for longer day sleeps as well.

At night-time you will ask your baby to resettle. To achieve this, you are best not to go in to her because this will stimulate her more and keep her awake longer. If at any point you feel you can not continue with this method and you want to go in to your baby, you will need to go in and lay her down and stay with her until she is asleep. Keep laying her down, which could be in excess of 40 times, until you notice it is taking her longer to stand up. At this point I recommend putting your hand on your baby's back or tummy when you lay her down. If she is trying to stand up, don't resist – take your hand away and continue to lay her down as before. But if she is staying down, keep your hand on her back or tummy as a reward. Only leave your hand there for a minute and then take it away again. Don't give up if your baby stands up again, just continue with the lay-down technique until your baby starts to stay down, then use your hand as a comfort again. Stay with your baby until she is asleep. Your presence may seem like an aid at this point, but after a few nights your baby will start to resettle without you there. Once again, please remember that the longer you can stay strong and leave your baby to resettle herself, the faster she will learn this skill. Going in may make you feel better but it will wake your baby up more.

The next few nights

On the second night of this approach, I recommend you only lay your baby down eight times before leaving when first putting her to bed, and only six times on the third night. After the third night I wouldn't lay her down again at all – it will be clear what you want her to do.

But a warning: just as you believe you are getting somewhere because your baby went down for her last sleep with little fuss, she will give you the biggest protest ever. This happens on about day three – and you will be able to win this because you are expecting it. Once you get past this hurdle, your sleep problems will be solved. It is as if all the babies I have worked with give one last, big attempt to win and be in charge of their parents, but after failing they decide to settle with no fuss from then on.

You must be strong and determined if you are to win this challenge, and you will. Don't let your baby be in control – you need to be in control to enable your baby to feel safe and secure in your care.

Important rules to follow

- When taking a dummy away (see next section), be strong and just do it. Don't be tempted to let your baby have one outside bedtime as this will cause confusion.

- Always leave the side of the cot up – never adjust it up or down when your baby is in it. This avoids creating a barrier between yourself and your baby, thereby allowing her to feel secure.

- Always leave the bedroom door open. Ensure you and your family don't tiptoe around, but carry on making your usual noise so that your baby can hear you. This will be reassuring for her and she won't shout as loudly.

- Put cuddly toys and muslin squares in the cot with your baby. She will not necessarily use these as sleep aids, but will likely throw them out of the cot in temper, allowing her to vent her anger. When putting cuddly toys in the cot as suggested here while teaching an older baby to self-settle, it is important to ensure that they are safe. Soft toys with bean filling could block the air from getting into a baby's mouth or nose if she was to sit it on top of her face. You also need to take care with fur-covered toys because the fur could be breathed in and cause a baby to cough a lot, which may not be dangerous but could cause a lot of unnecessary discomfort. To ensure the fur is safe, just pull at it and see if any comes away.

When to pull the plug

Very rarely a baby has got more willpower than you could ever imagine – I have come across only six babies in my whole life where you have to say enough is enough because the normal stages of tantrum/protesting crying just go on and on. I absolutely believe that it would do no emotional or psychological damage to a baby to protest for six or seven hours if that's what it takes for the tantrum to end; however, I would be concerned at the emotional and psychological damage it might do the parents or their relationship. Few parents, no matter how sleep-deprived or strong, could listen to a protest tantrum for over two and a half hours, so I tell parents of marathon runners to go in at that point and help their baby to sleep. Though not a perfect scenario, the protest needs to end, and giving up and getting the baby up would be a much worse outcome – it would teach her to yell and tantrum for two and a half hours to be picked up. So I believe going in and helping her to sleep is a good compromise.

Go in and, without eye contact or talking, lay your baby down every time she stands up until you notice she is taking longer to stand up. At this point I recommend putting your hand on her back or tummy when you lay her down. If your baby is trying to stand up, don't resist – take your hand away and continue to lay her down as before. But if she is staying down, keep your hand on her back or tummy as a reward. Only leave your hand there for a minute and then take it away again. Don't give up if she stands up again, just continue with the lay-down technique until your baby starts to stay down, then use your hand as a comfort again. Stay with your baby until she is asleep. Your presence may seem like an aid at this point, but there are few alternatives if you are going to solve these sleep problems. After a few of these challenges, your baby will start to fall asleep quickly after putting her in her cot. Remember you will need to be consistent to win the going-to-sleep confrontation.

If you have had to pull the plug on a marathon runner then you are best to only try to teach your baby to settle at 7 pm. Go for walks or drives during the day to help her to sleep. Once she is settling at night with little or no fuss, then take on the day sleep settling challenges.

Teaching a dummy-dependent baby to self-settle

If your baby needs a dummy to go to sleep I recommend you read my advice on whether to use a dummy on page 66. If you decide to remove the dummy, there are steps I recommend you follow in order to take it away and teach her to self-settle. First, I recommend you adhere as closely as possible to the proven 24-hour routine for your baby's age for a minimum of four days before you attempt to take the dummy away. Then on the fifth day, at the first sleep of the day, remove the dummy and follow my settling guide for your baby's age. You should throw all her dummies in the bin to ensure you are not tempted to use them again – even outside sleep times. Giving a baby their dummy outside sleep times will only cause confusion.

If your baby has a dummy but you rock, pat or feed her to get her to sleep, just take the dummy away on the first day of the routine, then take the other aid away on the fifth day. The reason for this is if your baby was really using the dummy as a sleep aid you would not need to help her with the second aid as well, so she is unlikely to be dependent on the dummy to go to sleep.

Felix's story

In the online advice area of the Save Our Sleep website I was asked the following question by Felix's mum: *I am rocking my three-month-old son Felix to sleep with a dummy every sleep. I am finding as he gets bigger this is harder to do. He is also having very short day sleeps. I would like to teach him to sleep without a dummy or the rocking. How can I do this?*

I explained to Felix's mum that there were a few simple steps she could take to teach Felix how to self-settle. The first thing to do was to make him feel safe and secure. I suggested putting him on a 24-hour routine for four days, settling him as she had before, but on the fifth day to stop the rocking and dummy use. As Felix was three months old, this was the routine and advice I suggested.

NIGHT FEEDS
Feed Felix when he wakes during the night. During night feeds, try not to talk to him and keep the lights dim, so he can see the difference between night and day.

7 am
Wake Felix up and feed him his milk feed. You'll need to wake him and feed him even if he last fed at 5.30 am, so he is always starting his day at the same time and on a full tummy.

9 am
Swaddle Felix over his safe sleeping bag and put him in bed on his back awake and allow him to self-settle.

11 am
If Felix is still asleep wake him up and feed him.

1 pm
Swaddle Felix over his safe sleeping bag and put him in bed on his back awake and allow him to self-settle.

3 pm
If Felix is still asleep wake him up and feed him.

4.30 pm

Go out for a walk or a drive to encourage Felix to sleep in places other than his bed. Remember to dress him as you would for bed and adjust his bedding to the outside temperature. Don't worry if he doesn't nap at this time as some babies only nap at this time every second day.

5.15 pm

Wake Felix up and give him a bath, or top-to-toe wash.

6 pm

Give Felix his milk feed.

7 pm

Swaddle Felix and put him in bed on his back awake and allow him to self-settle.

10.30 pm

Give Felix his dreamfeed.

On the fifth day, start with the 9 am sleep. Swaddle him over his safe sleeping bag and put him down in the cot on his back without a dummy. Allow him to protest for at least eight minutes from when he starts to cry, as he may stay quiet for a few minutes at first. When employing transitional sleeping tactics as recommended here, always time the period of crying, as one minute may seem like ten to you.

When he is crying, try listening for the kind of cry. If he is fighting sleep he will be using a protesting cry. A protesting cry is one with lots of changes in the sound. It might sound something like this: *Waaaaaa ... Pause ... Wa waaa waaa ... Pause ... Waa ... waa ... waaaaaaa ... Pause.* It will go up and down in pitch and there will be pauses in the wail. You should hear the pauses getting longer as Felix starts to fall asleep. If you are watching him, you will see him shut his eyes and nod off, then jump as he realises he is falling asleep, and cry again.

If there is a problem, for example if Felix has dirtied his nappy, his cry will be an emotional cry. The cry of an emotional or hungry baby is continuous with no pauses or changes in pitch or tone. It sounds like: *Waa, waa, waa, waa, waa, waa, waa, waa.* If Felix is crying emotionally, go in and get him up and look for a problem. If there is no visible problem, give him a cuddle and wind him for fifteen minutes before trying the self-settling again.

It is important to remember that crying is normal and it doesn't necessarily mean that something is seriously wrong. In teaching Felix to settle himself, inevitably there will be some crying. Felix's cries will become less frequent and shorter in duration as he develops the skills to settle himself. The challenge for you is to resist the temptation to comfort Felix every time he cries. If he cries for eight continuous minutes without any gaps of more than 30 seconds you might need to go in and help him to settle. You should move him onto his side, remembering to put him back on his back when he is asleep.

Try to avoid eye contact while moving and settling him. Leave Felix in the safe back-sleeping position and either pat or rub his tummy or alternatively you can stroke his forehead. If after 22 minutes from when you went in Felix has not settled, get him up and then after a ten-minute break start again with the eight-minute protest.

When Felix finally goes to sleep, he may wake again after just one sleep cycle. There's no need to get upset about this. Focus on the fact that he went to sleep in the first place. Don't expect him to have big sleeps or to resettle until he starts with little or no fuss at each sleep. In my experience, the most important part of teaching a baby to sleep without an aid such as a dummy or being rocked is following a routine. Combining the routines with the techniques I have described will help you teach Felix to self-settle, and he will begin having longer day sleeps in just a few days.

I recommend that if he wakes after just one sleep cycle during the day and you know he needs more sleep, get him up. Praise him for going to sleep in the first place and go for a walk or a drive to try to encourage him to sleep more in the recommended sleep time. A baby who does not have the skill to self-settle won't yet be able to resettle. At night-time you can go to him when he wakes and pick him up and feed him. After the feed, put him back to bed and settle him in the way I describe above.

Tips:

- Time the duration of your baby's protesting to reassure your-self that it is for less time than it seems.

- Set a mirror up at the door so you can watch your baby without being seen.

- Make sure the cot adheres to safety standards and is positioned safely in the bedroom.

- Your baby may wake again after the first sleep cycle at night-time. If this happens, be strong and use the settling advice I have given for night-waking for your baby's age.

An inconsistent approach

I often come across parents who try really hard to teach their baby to self-settle, but because they are not consistent they get nowhere and end up frustrated with a confused baby. Here's a couple of examples to help you understand what I mean by an inconsistent approach.

One-year-old Paul is waking a few times a night, and on his second or third wake is usually brought into his parents' bed. After deciding to use the lay-down approach to solve his sleep issues, Paul is put in his cot the first night and yells for 50 minutes before going to sleep. On the second night he yells for 30 minutes and he keeps improving each night until the fifth night when he doesn't even make a noise before going straight to sleep. From nights five to ten Paul puts himself to sleep and sleeps all night, every night. But on night eleven, he wakes just after his parents have got to sleep and yells for five minutes. Deciding they've had enough, they go and get him and let him spend the rest of the night in their bed. They don't think much of it but the next night, when Paul is put in his cot, he yells for over an hour before his parents give up again. In this type of case, the parents usually throw it in completely and then start over in a few weeks when they have had enough again. This is unfair on Paul who ends up getting very confused.

Another example would be parents who don't understand that a baby must first learn to go to sleep by herself before asking her to resettle. Quite often parents work really hard at keeping their baby on a routine while trying to solve a sleep problem, but they don't take on my resettling advice. These parents will have a good night of sleep from their baby and then put her down for a morning sleep, where she will fight slumber for five minutes but then only sleep for 40 minutes. Some parents find it really difficult to focus on the fact that their baby went to sleep; all they can see is she didn't sleep long enough so they decide to leave her in bed until she goes back to sleep. This is almost always a bad move because nine times out of ten she will not resettle. Instead she will protest for such a long time that in the end her parents give up, and all they have achieved is to teach their baby to protest until they come. The next time she is put down for a sleep she will try protesting for longer again to see if she is picked up.

Consistency is the key, so if you find you really can't be, then now is not the time to try to correct bad sleeping habits. Give up and try again a month or two down the track.

Lack of support from a partner

When teaching your baby new sleep habits, there is going to be some protesting. It is very distressing for a parent to listen to their baby protest, especially if it is in the middle of the night. I believe the hardest part is doing nothing because you know that by going in to your baby and giving her a pat or a comfort drink you could have her back asleep in a few minutes, but the protesting could go for a lot longer. You need to remember that going in is a short-term solution and yes, you will be back in bed asleep again faster, but you could also be woken every night for years to come. If you sit out the protesting you could all be sleeping all night every night from the next evening. How much better would that be?

One thing that has surprised me over the years is how many fathers I come across who find it impossible to hear their baby protest. I often assumed that mothers would be the 'soft' parent to deal with in these circumstances, but usually it is actually fathers I am trying to reassure when their baby is protesting. For a while I wondered if fathers often slept through the waking problems while mothers got up and settled the baby, and so they didn't feel the need to put their baby through the protests because they didn't see the problem. But I have since discovered this not to be the case. Quite often I come across fathers getting up in the night and settling the baby purely because they can't bear to listen to the baby's protests.

If you find yourselves in a situation where one of you is much stronger than the other at listening to your baby's protests, then consider sending the 'softer' partner away for a few nights, or at least to a distant room to sleep in! They can return in the day and, if possible, take part in the initial bedtime ritual so your baby can see it is a joint effort. The stronger of you may still need to ask a friend or relative to come around and give some support or even just company while you drink a few cups of tea. If one parent needs to work the next day it might also be best if they stayed somewhere else, and it may relieve some of the tension if you sent any older children away for the night too.

Sometimes a father pushes for the baby to be taught self-settling skills but the mother isn't ready. I tell my clients that it needs to be a joint effort. If you are fighting about the situation your baby will pick up on the tension and it would not be a good time to try changing her habits. The time will come when you are both ready.

BABY PAYBACK

It's amazing just how clever babies can be. I have come across some babies who will try anything to get out of going to bed.

Bowel movements after bedtime

James's story

The first time I realised babies were capable of doing a bowel movement to get out of bed was when I visited James, who was eleven months old at the time. His parents had tried controlled crying to settle him but it had got to the stage where each time James was put in his cot he would vomit.

We put him in his cot where we had laid out lots of towels to collect the vomit. When James vomited his mother went in and cleaned his face, picked up the soiled towels and walked out. All of this was done in complete silence with no eye contact.

We sat outside the door and listened in case there was a second vomit but soon realised James had done a bowel movement instead. After getting him up, changing his nappy and putting him back to bed, James did another poo. At this point we realised it was a game to James, so we waited until he was asleep and then went in and changed his nappy. This put an end to the game and when he realised we were not coming back in he was able to settle himself to sleep.

Since then I have seen lots of babies do bowel movements once put to bed. If the baby is changed before going straight to sleep then I see no problem in it. But if it is becoming a game and your baby is doing the smallest of poos so you have to change her ten times before sleep is achieved, then I suggest you don't go in until after she is asleep. Then, without taking your baby out of the cot, change her nappy. If she wakes up, which she well might, continue the change without speech or eye contact. Don't worry if you do not get her bottom perfectly clean – a little bit of poo will not do any harm between then and the morning.

Vomiting at bedtime

I often come across a baby who has learnt to vomit at bedtime during failed attempts at controlled crying. If you have one of these babies you will need to teach your child that vomiting will not get your attention or buy any extra time. This is hard, but it has to be done to stop the vomiting.

The way you achieve this is to make the bed vomit-proof. Layer towels in the bed and on the floor so it is easy for you to remove the vomit. When your baby vomits, go in and take the top towels away, leaving a second layer in case of a second vomit. If the vomit has gone on her clothing, undress her and put clean clothes on without taking her out of the cot by moving her from one end to the other. Do not make eye contact or talk to her while you do all of this and be calm and confident throughout, so you fool your baby into thinking you don't care about the vomit.

When she does go to sleep, remember to remove the extra towels in case she becomes tangled in them during the night. An alternative is to put your baby in a portable cot to begin with and, if she vomits, put her in the real cot.

COMMON QUESTIONS

My nine-month-old baby has been following your routines perfectly since birth, but for the past two weeks he is waking at 5.30 am every morning. I have been putting him back to bed at 8.30 am instead of 9 am to get through it, but what do you think is causing the early waking? I am not sure what would have caused the first 5.30 am waking but I do know you have been reinforcing it by putting him to bed at 8.30 am. For some reason I am yet to discover, babies of this age count all the sleep they get before 9.30 am as part of the twelve hours they should be getting at night. So I recommend you keep your baby up until 9.30 am before putting him back to bed for his morning sleep.

I am thinking of trying your lay-down technique but I am concerned that I will be too short to reach the bottom of my baby's cot. Should I put the cot side down even though you say not to? I have never come across this problem so you should give it a try first and see how you go. If you do find your height to be a problem you could put your hands through the bars, stand on a mattress on the floor so there is no chance you will fall off, or have the legs of the cot cut down so you can reach in to lay your baby down.

The first night using your approach, our baby Jack protested for 50 minutes at bedtime and slept until 6 am. On the second night he went to sleep in eight minutes but then woke up 46 minutes later and took a further twenty minutes to resettle. Does this mean

we are going backwards? Not at all – quite the opposite. The fact that Jack woke on the second night after 46 minutes is a good sign that his body is starting to get into proper sleep cycles. On the third night he may wake for a minute or two every two hours, which is again a really positive step – it means he is sleeping in the correct sleep cycle fashion.

I am going to stay with my sister so she can help me teach my baby of nine months to sleep all night. Is there anything I should do to prepare my baby? If you are going to stay with your sister it is very important to take your own portable cot with you so your baby will feel safe and secure in her sleeping environment. Use the portable cot for all your baby's sleeps in the day and night for two days before you go. The other benefit to this is that when you come home, your baby can still sleep in the portable cot and this will help you to be consistent in your settling approach. When she is sleeping well and adhering to the sleep times on my routine you can move her back into her usual cot. However, you should wait until the first sleep of the day to make this move.

You suggest always putting your baby to sleep where you intend for them to wake up. What happens if you need to go out and your baby is asleep? Would you wake her or move her to the pram? In certain circumstances you will need to move your sleeping baby. Recently, for example, I was with baby Grace. We put her to bed for her afternoon sleep and when it was time to leave for mothers' group, we lifted sleeping Grace and put her in her pram. After arriving at the group we were unable to take the pram in so we moved Grace, once again in her sleep, so that when she woke up she was lying in the middle of the mothers' group. Carefully moving a baby this way is acceptable because we would not have asked Grace to resettle if she had woken in a different place to where she had fallen asleep. We would also not have left her alone, so when she woke her mother was there to reassure her.

I am on day three of your deep-end approach with my fourteen-month-old baby and am thrilled because she slept eleven hours last night, which she has never done before. But today she is so clingy – should I worry? This is a normal phase, which will pass, that I believe happens for two reasons. First, if your baby is not used to getting much sleep overnight and is now sleeping eleven hours straight, believe it or not, she will be feeling really tired: I'm sure you have heard people say that the more sleep you have, the more you need. The second reason could be that your baby is used to lots of contact during the night and, now that this has gone, she may feel a little insecure. But don't worry, this will pass because as you too start to sleep better at night, which will not be for a few days, you will have more energy during the day to give her even more contact and attention.

My baby was waking twice a night for two hours at a time before starting your program. On the second night of the routine she woke every two hours and took between two and five minutes to go back to sleep each time. Is this normal? Yes, this is normal. It sounds like your baby never slept in proper sleep cycles. Now that she is learning the skills of self-settling, she is also starting to sleep in sleep cycles. You will see over the next couple of nights that the time she is awake between sleep cycles will decrease.

My baby falls asleep in a folded position. What should I do? During the day, leave him in this position but the moment you see him wake up, even if it is only after twenty minutes sleep, get him up and praise him for going to sleep by himself. If he fell asleep in this position at night-time, go in after ten minutes and move him just enough to straighten his legs out to ensure his safety and to make sure he doesn't wake from being uncomfortable. He may well wake when you move him but better he does so and resettles then than just after you go to bed.

My baby is one year old and goes to sleep without any fuss. At night he sleeps all night but in the day he only ever sleeps 40 minutes. Do you have any answers? I have come across this a few times and in most cases found there to be a difference in the sleeping environment in the day compared to the night. For example, one baby was put in his sleeping bag at night but not in the day; we put him in his sleeping bag in the day and the problem disappeared.

What happens if my toddler sleeps all night for three weeks after using one of your approaches and then suddenly wakes crying during the night? Do we leave him to cry himself back to sleep or do we go and comfort him? If your baby usually sleeps all night and the waking is out of the blue, I suggest you go in and get him up. Bring him out of his room and comfort him. If you think there may be a problem such as an earache or fever, give him whatever medication you usually use and keep him up for a minimum of twenty minutes while it 'kicks in' then put him back to bed and leave him to settle himself. If your baby has a fever, please follow my advice for a sick baby (chapter 12).

I put my toddler to bed each night at 7 pm but can't get her to sleep past 6 am. It is not due to her morning sleep as she only has a lunchtime nap. Should I try putting her to bed later? No, I suggest you try an earlier bedtime of, say 6.30 pm. Your baby may be waking early due to overtiredness and if she gets more sleep, she may actually sleep longer.

Could the light be waking my baby up? I have never found the need to use blackout blinds or to always darken the room a baby sleeps in so no, I don't believe light would be affecting your baby.

What happens if I am trying to get my baby to resettle early in the morning and she yells for hours? You should always try to stick it out longer than your baby can yell at you. Sometimes, however, it does go on so long that you feel you can't take any more. If this happens to you, wait until your baby takes a break in the yelling and go in during the break to get her up. Never give in while your baby is yelling at you.

10

BREAKS TO THE ROUTINE

With the busy lives we live these days, there are often times when you have to change your child's routine to allow for things such as returning to work, putting the clocks forward and back, holidays and travel. The best way to approach these issues is to plan ahead. This chapter is to help you adjust for the different situations you are bound to come across in your baby's first years.

VISITORS

If you have relatives or friends who always seem to pop in at bedtime, explain to them how important your seven o'clock bus is (even if it means giving them this book to read!) Ask them to come earlier or at the weekend if they want to see your baby or toddler. Or, if they are coming to see you, ask them to come after eight when baby or toddler is in a deeper sleep and won't be disturbed. This also applies to other parents who walk in the door from a day at work at 6.59 pm – they would be better to sneak in a few minutes later.

If you are having guests to stay then it is best to explain to them how you handle things with your baby or toddler at bedtime or in the night. I have even heard of a baby who has not had a night feed for weeks until a visiting grandparent heard the baby stir one night and gave him a bottle, thinking she was doing everyone a favour. Please talk to your visitors and explain to them that they might hear your baby at night but they don't need to worry. If all else fails and you find yourself helping a baby to sleep, you may just have to correct some sleep problems when you get your house back to yourselves.

TRAVELLING WITH A BABY OR TODDLER

Travelling with a baby or toddler is very different from travelling alone. The main difference is you will need to plan things well in advance. When clients of mine contact me with concerns about travelling, the first thing I always tell them is that they will need to get their child settled into a good routine a few weeks before the trip. I have clearly observed over years of sleep consulting that children in a routine adapt faster and more easily to any new environment. This applies equally to children that are travelling across time zones or within their usual time zone.

It is also important that your baby feels safe and secure wherever you ask him to sleep, so I recommend you always bring your own portable travel cot. If you don't have one then try to borrow one from a friend or rent one a week before you go so you can test it and take it with you. Believe me, it is well worth it. The last thing you need is to find the hotel has run out of cots or your baby can jump out of one that is supplied. I advise that you put your baby into the travel cot two nights before your trip so he can get used to it. This will lessen the impact of the new environment.

Travel by car

If you are going to travel a long distance by car, it is often easier to begin the journey at your baby's sleep time. I find the easiest plan is to set off at 6.30 pm, just after his last feed for the night. He should happily sleep for most of the journey. The driver should try to get a nap in before leaving. Longer journeys should be broken up with a stop for the night. If your baby has become familiar with the portable cot, this will not be a problem. Another good option for younger babies is to get under way first thing in the morning and drive through the morning and midday sleeps, stopping for his feeds and your lunch to break up the journey. If your baby is still having a dreamfeed, don't worry about stopping for it right on the scheduled time – you just need to do it within the hour it is due. It is much more important to find a safe place to stop rather than watching the clock.

When travelling by car, always pack a small bag that is easy to get to rather than having to stop and go looking in the boot for something. Remember, some babies can get sick on long journeys so be prepared. Travelling by car is generally easier than planes, trains or buses because you can bring a lot more of the accessories you need to keep baby happy.

Car seats

You will need a car seat every time you put your baby in the car, it doesn't matter how short the journey. Don't under any circumstances put a seat belt around you and your baby: if you are in an accident your body weight pushing against your baby and the seat belt could kill him, even if it is just a little bump.

If you acquire a secondhand baby seat, try to find out its full history – if it seems damaged or has been involved in an accident, don't use it. Car seats should by purchased and updated depending on your baby's weight, not age.

Always double-check what weight your baby or child is and the weight guidelines on the car seat you are thinking of putting them in. Recent research has shown that the safest travelling position for a baby up until twelve months of age is in a rear-facing car seat. If you are not sure how to fit your baby's seat, have a professional baby restraint fitter install it. Of course, the chances of being involved in an accident are relatively small, but if you are then the chances of being injured are high.

Travel by aeroplane

Travelling on aeroplanes can be challenging and needs a lot more planning. Make sure to call the airline before you travel and book bassinet-equipped seats for younger babies, but also be prepared to not have access to these. Airlines often have to change plans at the last minute, so don't be disappointed if for some reason the bassinet is no longer available. Always remember to keep your baby very warm during the flight as this will help him to sleep in the air-conditioned air.

As far as routines for babies go, I generally recommend giving your baby a milk feed two hours before the plane is due to take-off or land so that he will be hungry enough to take breast or bottle on the plane (a sucking baby's ears will be more comfortable during take-offs and landings). For example, if you are booked on a 4 pm flight, feed your baby at 2 pm rather than the usual 3 pm feed so when you offer your baby milk after take-off at 4 pm he will take it.

With a younger baby, try to check your pram in with your luggage as having your baby in a sling or backpack frees up your hands to get organised when boarding and trying to put cabin baggage away. But when travelling with a toddler you will probably need a pushchair to avoid him running all over the airport, or to have a nap in if there are any delays. You will usually need to check it in just before boarding, however.

If your baby is on formula, it is a good idea to bring the water and powder separately as it is not always possible to keep prepared milk at a cool enough temperature on a plane. Even if you give it to cabin crew to keep in the fridge, I have seen it left out for long periods while they are serving food. You should also bring extra formula or food in case of delays, or your baby may waste more than usual if he is feeling a bit funny on the flight. If you are breastfeeding then bring some extra food for yourself and bottles of water.

When you get there

Irrespective of your mode of travel, when you get to your final destination you may have to keep your baby awake for a little bit longer on the first night if he slept well during the journey. It is very important that you follow your normal routine at bedtime so your baby recognises all the sleep cues. If you are staying with friends or relatives, ask them to make themselves scarce on the first couple of nights so your baby doesn't get over-stimulated. On the first morning, put your baby straight back onto his normal routine at local time if you have crossed time zones, regardless of how often or how early he woke the previous night or that morning. If you find your baby is waking a lot more at night, try to settle him with some water and a cuddle, but if after a couple of nights this is starting to look habitual, try leaving him for ten minutes before you go to him.

Once all is settled and your baby is happily into his routine again, you can adjust the routine to help you enjoy your holiday more. The key to altering my routines is to try to avoid doing so two days in a row so your baby doesn't become overtired. If you find you have adjusted things without causing a problem, try it for two days in a row. And remember that your baby doesn't have to be in his cot at sleep times, just in a comfortable sleeping place, but do try to give him a comforter at all sleep times. If you find your baby is taking short naps rather than full sleeps while on holidays, don't worry; try putting him to bed at night a little bit earlier.

Quite often parents find that their baby sleeps much better away from home if they are in a warmer climate, as the additional heat tends to assist them to sleep. If you plan to take your baby out at night so you can enjoy a meal, try to encourage an extra nap in the late afternoon as this will make him happier while you are trying to eat.

Finally, don't worry too much if your baby gets totally off his routine. It will only take a couple of uninterrupted days when you get home to sort things out.

Tips:

- If you need to sterilise, just take some soluble sterilising tablets and buy a cheap bucket when you get there that can be left behind afterwards.

- I advise putting your baby into the portable cot for two nights before your trip so he can get used to sleeping in his new cot. This will lessen the impact of the new environment.

Moving house

Moving house does not have to cause a big disruption to your baby's or toddler's sleep patterns. The most important thing you need to do when moving house is make your baby or toddler feel as safe and secure as possible, and the easiest way to achieve this is to have your baby or toddler in a good feeding and sleeping routine. They like to know what is going to happen and when.

It is very important that your baby or toddler is in the same bed in the new house, so if you are not going to be able to set up the usual cot by the time your child has his first sleep in there, I recommend you put your baby in a portable cot and that he sleeps in it for the four nights previous to the move. It is a good idea to take your baby or toddler for a tour of the new house and explain to him where everyone's room is and where you will be sleeping.

Ensure your baby or toddler's routine is the same coming up to bedtime, so if you usually give your baby his last feed yourself, do so, even if there's an extra set of hands around. It will all go more smoothly if you give your baby or toddler the normal amount of attention. Remember, if bedtime goes well, you will have lots of uninterrupted hours to unpack.

If your baby has always been a good sleeper and suddenly wakes in the night it is all right to go in and comfort him or give a sick baby medicine and then leave. However, if he has not been a good sleeper from day one and you have had to teach him how to sleep I do not recommend the above approach. Instead, go in and lift your baby from his bed and bring him out of his room to comfort him or give him medicine. After ten minutes, if there is no obvious problem, put him back into bed so he can put himself back to sleep. If you decide to give your baby medicine keep him up for twenty minutes until the medicine starts to work before putting him back to bed.

My reason for this is if you walked in and checked your baby and then left, you would be asking him to resettle after seeing you; this would cause your baby to get very emotional and he may not settle. If you get him up and then put him back to bed you are asking him to settle, not resettle.

Your baby or toddler may want to test the rules and boundaries in this new house so it is very important to give clear messages that the rules are the same. This will make them feel safer. But if, for example, after putting your baby or toddler to bed on the first night he became very upset and was obviously crying emotionally, go and get him up and bring him out of the bedroom to calm and comfort before putting him back to bed. Whatever you do, I don't advise going in and then walking out again, as this is controlled crying and will make your baby or toddler more upset.

If you are moving to a country with a substantial time difference, follow my advice for travelling with a baby. Moving overseas is actually easier than going on holidays as you won't have to adjust your baby again when you get home.

Bottle refusal and returning to work

If you have been following this book from the beginning of your baby's life, then you are probably already preparing yourself and your baby for the day you return to work simply by adhering to the routines. Even if you are not positive you will be returning to work, there are still a few things you should be doing from the first few weeks. It is easier to have a baby ready for this transition just in case than to keep putting the idea off and one day have to face reality and try to prepare an older baby.

The most important thing to be aware of is bottle refusal. I get hundreds of calls and emails every year from parents who need to return to work and their baby refuses a bottle or refuses to take the bottle from anyone other than the mother or father. If you have only ever breastfed your baby, don't expect that your baby will take it; 99 times out of 100, a baby who has only ever had breastfeeds will refuse point-blank to take a bottle.

I don't think these babies are trying to be in control, they are just so secure in the way things are that this sudden change frightens them. Babies are creatures of habit: they like things done the same way each and every day and they also like them done at a regular time. In a similar way, a young child watches the same DVD over and over because they like to know what is going to happen and when. So if you know you are going to be returning to work or even if there is a slim chance you will be, try to introduce the bottle in the first two weeks and keep giving at least one a day. If your baby is bottle-fed, get him used to other people feeding him the bottle a few weeks before you return to work.

If you need to return to work now and this advice comes too late, all is not lost, but some bottle-taking techniques work better than others. I have had parents contact me who have tried all sorts of ways to get their baby to take a bottle, one of which was to starve their baby of any breastmilk or solids until they take a bottle. I totally disagree with this approach as you will end up with one very tired, hungry and maybe even dehydrated baby, and you will most likely get nowhere. I tried it myself about eleven years ago with a little baby called Tom, purely because I knew no better and was doing what I had read in a book. I tried all day to give Tom a bottle and was having no luck when my sister Suzanne took over; within a minute, Tom was drinking. The difference was Suzanne's confident approach, saying to Tom that he was going to take the bottle from her even if she had to sit there all night, starkly different to my 'softly, softly' approach. From that day I have used her technique and only once has it taken me more than an hour to get a baby to take a bottle.

The way I recommend giving your baby his first bottle is to initially adhere to the 24-hour routine for his age for at least a week before you try. Then start telling your baby that in so many days you will be giving him the bottle – you may be surprised at how much a baby understands. (If you think about it, a puppy by ten weeks can be aware of what the word 'walk' means, so I don't for a second believe a baby of around six months would not understand when you say you will be giving him a bottle.)

The best time to start on the bottle is with the first feed in the morning at 7 am. Be prepared for what may be a long and tough challenge with your baby. Sit down in a comfortable position (you may be there for a few hours) with your baby on your lap, look him straight in the eye and say, 'I know you don't want to take this bottle, but you need to.' Tell him the reasons behind needing him to take the bottle. If you are going into hospital, tell him; if you are returning to work, tell him that. Then tell him that you are prepared to sit there for a week if you need to, but you are not giving up until he has drunk some of the bottle.

Next put the bottle in your baby's mouth and talk to him the whole time, reassuring him it is all right. He may be crying and upset, scared of the bottle and the feeling of the teat in his mouth.

You need to be confident and reassuring and to also keep telling him it is all right and he needs to drink. Don't take the bottle out of his mouth. It might get a bit boring or tiring, so I usually start to sing to the baby both to pass the time and to make him feel better. You might be surprised at how soon he starts to drink or you might have to sit there for a number of hours, although since I have learnt not to take the bottle out I have never had to sit with a baby for more than 35 minutes. If you are sitting for more than an hour you will need to change to a fresh bottle.

As soon as he starts to suck, praise him and let him know how much he is pleasing you by sucking. When he stops, take the bottle out. Try him again with the bottle a few seconds later but as before. It is all right if he only drinks as little as 25 ml (0.8 oz) altogether. Give up if he won't take any more and continue with your daily routine. If your baby is on solids and the time you normally give them has passed, have them now. If his bedtime has passed, put him to bed. If it is not yet time for solids or sleep, wait till the correct time and follow the routine. At the next milk feed of the day, give another bottle in the same way as the first.

Many breastfeeding mothers who take on this bottle challenge, because, for example, they are returning to work, would like to continue to breastfeed their baby in the morning and at night but are scared to in case the baby refuses the bottle again. Unfortunately, only you can make this decision and it is a hard one. But one thing to remember is that if you are not entirely sure what your plans are, it makes sense to express to keep your milk supply until you are.

If your baby is going into day care, you could ask the staff to follow your routine. Be sure they understand how you settle your baby at home, but don't worry if they do things very differently as your baby will soon learn that there is one set of boundaries at home and a different set at day care. It is easier for a baby to adjust to care if he is in it more frequently, not less, so if you take him to care on a Monday and then not again until Thursday, it will take your baby a lot longer to adjust than if he went three days in a row. If you are having someone come into your home to mind your little ones then ask them to follow your routine.

DAYLIGHT-SAVING

Parents of older children generally welcome the arrival of British Summer Time (BST) as it allows them to spend a little more time outside in the evening. However, with younger children there is a downside as the changing times can interfere with little body clocks and therefore sleeping habits. Adults can quite easily adapt to a new wake-up time and bedtime – especially if they are already a little sleep-deprived – but in young children and babies it can be more difficult.

Moving the clocks forward by one hour at the beginning of BST means that if you want to keep the same sleeping schedules and get baby off to bed at 7 pm, you may now be putting him to sleep in daylight. This gets a lot of parents worried and can be a little distracting for the baby, but I have never in fact found it to be a problem. In my experience, daylight makes no difference to a baby who has been taught the skills to put himself to sleep. I have also clearly observed that children on a routine adapt faster and more easily to any time change (this applies equally to children travelling across time zones and is one of the reasons I always advise people to establish a good routine a few weeks before a trip).

Meanwhile, the other end of the equation is that children or babies who are early risers may be now waking their parents at 6 am instead of 5 am, which can actually be quite helpful.

Making the daylight-saving transition: a guide

I find it easier to adjust the times over the two days leading up to the clock change, and this also minimises the effect on a baby or child. But as every baby and child is different, the daylight-saving guide below should only be used as a reference point and you may need to tailor it to suit your baby's needs and your family dynamic. The following uses the routine for babies aged ten weeks until you introduce solids as an example to help explain the process.

On Friday morning wake your baby as normal at 7 am and follow your normal daily routine until 2.40 pm. At this point, if he is still sleeping, wake him for what would have been his 3 pm feed. For the rest of the day, complete the routine twenty minutes earlier than you would otherwise. This should pan out to putting your baby to bed at 6.40 pm instead of 7 pm. This means you will be doing the dreamfeed twenty minutes early as well.

On Saturday, get him up at 6.40 am to feed and continue the rest of the routine twenty minutes early. Wake him up (if necessary) at 2.20 pm in order to have what was the 3 pm feed. Now you have shifted the routine by 40 minutes over two days. Once again, follow your normal routine from here but everything will be 40 minutes early, so you will put your baby to bed at 6.20 pm instead of 7 pm.

On Sunday, when the clocks move forward, wake him up at the new 7 am (which was 6 am before British Summer Time began) and follow the normal routine using the new times.

AN EXAMPLE OF MAKING THE TRANSITION TO DAYLIGHT-SAVING: TEN WEEKS UNTIL SOLIDS ROUTINE

	Thursday	Friday	Saturday	Sunday
Feed	7 am	7 am	6.40 am	7 am (6 am old time)
Sleep	9 am	9 am	8.40 am	9 am (8 am)
Feed	11 am	11 am	10.40 am	11 am (10 am)
Sleep	1 pm	1 pm	12.40 pm	1 pm (12 noon)
Feed	3 pm	2.40 pm	2.20 pm	3 pm (2 pm)
Nap	4.30 pm	4.10 pm	3.50 pm	4.30 pm (3.30 pm)
Bath	5.15 pm	4.55 pm	4.35 pm	5.15 pm (4.15 pm)
Feed	6.30 pm	6.10 pm	5.50 pm	6.30 pm (5.30 pm)
Bedtime	7 pm	6.40 pm	6.20 pm	7 pm (6 pm)
Dreamfeed	10.30 pm	10.10 pm	9.50 pm	10.30 pm (9.30 pm)

The process works almost exactly the same in reverse when daylight-saving ends. On the Thursday before the clocks go back, give your baby his last feed ten minutes later than usual then put him to bed at 7.10 pm.

On Friday morning get him up when he wakes but if he sleeps in, leave him until 7.20 am. If he wakes before 7.20 am, try not to feed him until this time but don't worry if you have to feed him earlier because you will get back on track as the day goes by. Follow your normal routine but this time twenty minutes later than usual, so at 9.20 am he will be off to bed and the next feed will be at 11.20 am. At the last feed of the day, feed him 30 minutes later than usual and put him to bed at 7.40 pm.

On Saturday, if he doesn't wake by himself, leave it until 7.40 am to wake him for his feed. If he is awake, try not to feed him until 7.40 am. Again, don't worry if he can't last until 7.40 am – give yourself some peace and try to adjust the feeds through the course of the day. Then it is a case of following the routine 40 minutes later than usual all day until the last feed, which should be done 50 minutes later than you usually would. Put him in bed at 8 pm on the changeover night, which should allow him to sleep until the 'new' 7 am when daylight-saving ends the following morning. If he is awake earlier, try not to feed him until 7 am.

This transition may take a few more days but the principle of slowly adjusting the baby or child rather than expecting them to cope all of a sudden applies. Within a week it all should be fine.

As an aside, daylight-saving time changes are also a useful milestone to check or change the batteries in your smoke alarm, check the use-by dates on all your medicines, and check the batteries in your baby monitors and other alarms. While in the seasonal-change mode, you could also have a look at the adjustable harness straps in your baby's car seat and check they are in the correct position for his size.

AN EXAMPLE OF MAKING THE TRANSITION FROM DAYLIGHT-SAVING: TEN WEEKS UNTIL SOLIDS ROUTINE

	Thursday	Friday	Saturday	Sunday
Feed	7 am	7.20 am	7.40 am	7 am (8 am old time)
Sleep	9 am	9.20 am	9.40 am	9 am (10 am)
Feed	11 am	11.20 am	11.40 am	11 am (12 noon)
Sleep	1 pm	1.20 pm	1.40 pm	1 pm (2 pm)
Feed	3 pm	3.20 pm	3.40 pm	3 pm (4 pm)
Nap	4.30 pm	4.50 pm	5.10 pm	4.30 pm (5.30 pm)
Bath	5.15 pm	5.35 pm	5.55 pm	5.15 pm (6.15 pm)
Feed	6.40 pm	7 pm	7.20 pm	6.30 pm (7.30 pm)
Bedtime	7.10 pm	7.40 pm	8 pm	7 pm (8 pm)
Dreamfeed	10.40 pm	11 pm	11.20 pm	10.30 pm (11.30 pm)

COMMON QUESTIONS

People have suggested giving our six-month-old baby something to help him sleep on a fourteen-hour flight. What do you think? I do not advise medicating a baby to help him sleep on a long flight, and you will find your baby will sleep a lot on the flight anyway due to the air conditions in the cabin. It could be very dangerous if he had a reaction to what you gave him and you were so far away from medical help.

We are thinking of taking the dummy away from our four-month-old baby but we will also be moving house in six weeks. When would be the best time to take it away? I suggest you do it now.

If you have your baby self-settling and in a good routine, the move will be much easier on everyone.

If I put my baby in day care, will the way they settle him to sleep affect his sleeping at home? I have always found that babies learn very quickly that there are one set of rules at day care and another set at home so have never found this to cause a problem. Quite often I see babies who are having one day sleep at day care but two sleeps at home without any difficulty.

11

SPECIAL
SITUATIONS

When talking about special situations I am talking about factors that may affect your ability to follow my advice exactly as I give it in this book. In this chapter I will advise you how to follow my advice if your child has a disability, chronic illnesses or you are living in crowded accommodation or you have stepchildren visiting you. I have included in this chapter the most common disabilities and chronic illnesses that might affect your child's sleep. These include asthma, Down's syndrome, eczema, hyperactive children and sleep apnoea. I have also tried to include a few other conditions which you may not have to worry about for a few years such as nightmares, night terrors, sleep walking and talking because it is always better to be prepared for what might happen.

BABIES WITH DISABILITIES OR CHRONIC ILLNESSES
If your baby has a disability or a long-term health problem, she will require a lot of extra attention and time from you. I believe it is just as important for these babies to benefit from clear boundaries such as having a good routine, encouraging good sleep habits and instilling bedtime rituals. It is of course much more difficult to be firm with a baby who is unwell or suffering in some way, and parents of these babies naturally feel great worry or concern. But a consequence of this different treatment can be some very bad habits. Find out very early if

you should be treating your baby any differently at sleep times – the best person to ask is your baby's doctor. If your doctor agrees, practise good sleep habits from day one and use my settling techniques for your baby's age or development stage.

Asthma

Babies with asthma tend to experience fragmented sleep, especially if their symptoms are poorly controlled. They are likely to wake with episodes of coughing, wheezing and breathlessness in the night. Many parents are too worried to leave a baby with asthma to protest for any length of time because they worry it may trigger an attack. I can understand this but feel that every baby and child needs to learn how to put themselves to sleep.

It is important that your baby's asthma is controlled with adequate medication and that she is 'stable' before you begin to think about changing sleep habits. When this is the case, talk to your doctor about whether he or she feels your baby is healthy enough to do so.

Asthma is an illness that cannot be cured in the traditional sense, but it can be effectively controlled. While many babies outgrow their asthma, others learn how to manage their condition and do what other children do, such as running, swimming and playing. Either way, you can be assured that most children with asthma grow up to be healthy adults.

Although there is no cure, there are ways you can help to prevent attacks. Keep your baby's room as dust-free as possible to deter dust mites from being inhaled. Dust mites survive and thrive on minute particles of human skin. Things you can do to try to keep the mites at bay include taking up any carpet in your baby's room and covering hardwood floors with rugs which can then be cleaned on a regular basis. All your baby's bedding should be 100 per cent cotton or bamboo and washed at the hottest temperature possible once a week. Take all stuffed toys out of her room and machine wash them frequently. Let your baby spend as much time outdoors as possible: wrap her up when it's cold or put on sunscreen and a hat when it's hot, then go outside. As asthma is more common in homes with gas cookers, use a fan when you're cooking with a gas hob. Avoid having an open fire or wood-burning stove. Although the warmth is inviting, the smoke may irritate your baby's respiratory system.

> **Tip:** Please see advice on page 230 for tips to help prevent asthma attacks.

Down's syndrome

Babies with Down's syndrome tend to experience the usual sleeping problems of settling at bedtime and waking in the night. If your baby is healthy in every other way, use my settling advice for her development stage. Usually when I am working with a baby of twelve months with Down's syndrome who is not yet standing, I use the settling advice for a six-month-old.

However, these babies are also particularly prone to obstructive sleep apnoea syndrome (OSAS). Babies suffering from this syndrome are frequently disrupted during sleep when their upper airway becomes blocked, preventing them from breathing. They then (unsurprisingly) wake up, needing to breathe. This can happen hundreds of times each night, resulting in restlessness, loud snoring, coughing and choking noises. The cause of the problem should be investigated by an ear, nose and throat specialist or a sleep investigation unit, who may recommend treatment. This may involve the removal of tonsils and adenoids, a relatively simple procedure.

Eczema

Babies with eczema often have real difficulties sleeping at night. It is very important to teach babies with eczema to self-settle because the stress of not sleeping deeply can exacerbate the condition. Babies with eczema find it especially difficult to settle once they wake in the night with hot, itchy skin, so the process of drifting from one sleep cycle to the next is harder than it is for a baby without eczema. Aiding your baby to get from one sleep cycle to the next may seem like a good idea at the time but in the long run will cause ongoing sleep problems that will at some stage need correcting, so the sooner you address these issues the better for you both.

If your child suffers from eczema or asthma, you will need to try and limit their contact with dust mites and other irritants. Here are some key tips to remember:

- Try to make the nursery a room with hard floors rather than fitted carpets.

- Use cotton or bamboo bed linen/sleeping bags and nightwear – avoid synthetic fibres.

- Use non-biological washing powder or liquid and avoid fabric conditioners. You should wash all the cotton or bamboo bedding including sleeping bags and clothing at 60°C to kill the dust mites as well as vacuuming the bedding regularly.

- Keep the nursery curtains as clean as possible.

- Allow no pets in the nursery.

- Put all soft toys or comforters in the freezer overnight every other night.

- Don't let your baby with eczema get too hot at night as this will make her itchier. Make sure her cot or bed isn't against a radiator to avoid her getting too hot but also don't let her get so cold she can't sleep.

- Ask your GP to prescribe a cream and medicated bath oil for your baby with eczema. Never use normal baby bubble baths or creams on your baby's skin.

Once you feel you have done all you can to control the eczema, use my normal settling advice for your baby's age to teach her to self-settle.

Flat head syndrome (Plagiocephaly)

Flat head syndrome (deformational plagiocephaly or positional plagio-cephaly) is common in newborn babies and refers to a misshapen or uneven head shape. Deformational plagiocephaly is present at birth and may be caused by the baby's position during pregnancy, or movement of the soft skull bones in the birthing process. The uneven shape will usually rectify itself within six weeks; however, sometimes a baby's head does not return to a normal shape and the baby may have developed a flattened spot at the back or side of the head. This condition is known as deformational plagiocephaly.

Positional plagiocephaly occurs during the first few weeks or months of life. If a baby lies in the same position for long periods of time, her head may flatten in one area due to the thin and flexible bone structure in newborn babies' heads. There is some suggestion that this is becoming more common because babies are now placed on their backs to sleep to reduce the risk of cot death. This may be the case so there are measures you should take to prevent flat head syndrome by varying your baby's head position while asleep and awake. It is important to monitor your baby's head shape and if you think there is a problem see your doctor or paediatrician before four months, as the older the baby, the longer and less effective the treatment is.

Even with the increased number of babies suffering from flat head syndrome, the World Health Organisation is still recommending babies are safer and at less risk of cot death if placed on their back to sleep.

- **Sleeping position:** Always put your baby to sleep on her back to reduce the risk of cot death, but alternating your baby's head from the left to right side will help to even out the shape of her head. This is perfectly safe as your baby is still lying on her back, you are just turning her head to the side.

- **Cot:** Alternate the ends of the cot where you place your baby to sleep or change the position of the cot in the room routinely to encourage her to look at different objects in her room.

- **Comforter:** If you are following my swaddling advice (pages 64–66) for your baby of under six months and you have one of my safe approved comforters (pages 68–70) then one tactic you might find useful is to alternate which side you place your baby's comforter each sleep to encourage her to look to both the left and to the right.

- **Tummy time:** This is very important as it encourages your baby to lift her head, thus lessening the effects of flat head syndrome. You could also lay her on her side if she is unable to hold her head up.

- **Carrying your baby:** If you use a sling to carry your baby, try to hold her upright. Alternatively, you can carry her over your arm on her tummy, so her head does not have any pressure on it.

You must consult your health visitor or GP if you have any concerns about your baby's head shape. This is also the case if your baby is only able to turn her head to one side when lying on her back. Flat head syndrome often corrects without any treatment at all as the baby grows and, more importantly, is able to sit up, but if treatment is required, it is very important that your baby receives it before her first birthday while her head is still soft. If treatment is deemed necessary, the two types available are counter-positioning and corrective helmets. Counter-positioning works well until your baby gets strong enough to overcome the positioning technique (usually at about four to five months). After that age a helmet is the treatment of choice for moderate to severe plagiocephaly.

Counter-positioning
This procedure simply means getting the weight of your baby's head off the flat spot for 90 per cent of the time. It also helps to alternate her head from side to side and to the middle while she is lying on her back. As previously mentioned, tummy time and lying your baby on her side while awake are also very important. To learn how to apply counter-positioning to your baby, talk to your health visitor or paediatric physiotherapist.

Corrective helmets
If you are concerned about your baby's head shape have it checked by a family doctor or paediatrician who will be able to assess the need for a corrective helmet. If counter-positioning does not help, 'cranial remodelling' helmets may be recommended for more severe cases.

The helmet is designed to remove the pressure around the skull, which assists the head to grow into the correct shape. Intended for babies under one year, it is lightweight and lined with foam for your baby's comfort. It is worn anywhere from two to six months and needs to be adjusted about once a fortnight. The helmet needs to be worn for 23 hours a day but may be removed at bath time.

Hyperactive children

If you have a baby or toddler with a long-term sleep problem, the likelihood is that they are extremely exhausting because the less sleep a child gets, the more hyperactive they become. Active children (more commonly boys) also tend to sleep less than placid types. A child who is diagnosed as either being hyperactive or having Attention Deficit Hyperactivity Disorder (ADHD) finds it especially hard to wind down enough to fall asleep easily. My routines will really help if you have a child who fits into this category as these children benefit from boundaries. These boundaries should stay absolutely consistent night after night.

For parents who find setting boundaries hard, having a child who needs strict guidelines can sometimes result in clashes. The key thing to remember when this happens is to keep calm and confident. Speak to your child in a firm, calm voice at all times and try to have the whole family calm as well at least an hour before bedtime. Try playing some classical music, and never have the television on leading up to bedtime.

There will be other parents in your area dealing with similar issues – ask your doctor or clinic nurse for a support group you can join.

Sleep apnoea

Sleep apnoea is a relatively rare breathing disorder which is also known as obstructive sleep apnoea syndrome (OSAS). The word apnoea stems from the Greek for lack of breath and describes a condition where a blockage in the throat obstructs the breathing pattern and affects the way a sufferer breathes and sleeps. It's often caused by enlarged adenoids (glands in the throat just behind the nose) and tonsils, and when the muscles relax at night the oversized glands can temporarily block air to the lungs.

As you can imagine, this is a very frightening thing for a child to experience but it is treatable. The most obvious symptom of sleep apnoea is loud snoring, often with pauses of up to a few seconds in breathing while asleep. Other symptoms you might notice in a sleeping child include gasping or choking noises during the night, sleeping in a very restless way and sweatiness. When your child is awake she will often be emotional and irritable, always showing tired signs.

Remember that not every child who snores will have this condition: about ten in every 100 children snore and not all of them will have sleep apnoea. Sleep apnoea affects most child sufferers between three and six years, because tonsils and adenoids are at their largest in comparison to child-sized airways.

If you think your child might have sleep apnoea, start by telling your GP about it. If he or she thinks you have reason to be concerned you will be referred to an ear, nose and throat specialist, who may decide your child's tonsils or adenoids need to be removed. In most cases this relatively simple operation does the trick. Sometimes allergies or being overweight could be behind your child's apnoea, but your GP will be able to tell you if this is the case.

SLEEP DISCREPANCIES IN CHILDREN

Quite often I will get an email or phone call from a parent I haven't heard from in years telling me that their perfect sleeper has started to disturb them at night, with the child frequently sleeping through the disturbance so she cannot recall it in the morning. Below are some of the most common causes I come across in these situations and the advice I give to parents. A common factor in all the below sleep discrepancies is overtiredness or a full bladder. Try to ensure that your child goes to bed early and empties her bladder each night 30 minutes before bedtime and then again just a minute before bed. It is also a good idea to limit drinks one hour before bed as part of your bedtime routine.

Nightmares

Most children experience nightmares at some stage. They normally occur in the last two-thirds of the night, after midnight and before 7 am, and are more common in families who have a history of nightmares. Nightmares are unlikely to be linked with any emotional problems and will normally stop happening without any help needed. If you have a child who is having nightmares, the first thing I would advise is to stop your child from watching nearly all television as this is often a trigger. Sometimes nightmares can be a learnt attention-seeking behaviour – having a nightmare one night got so much attention that they decide to pretend to have more. Banning television and explaining to your child that it is because it is giving her nightmares can often discourage her from pretending to have them.

Sometimes children wake up screaming, repeating phrases like 'go away' or 'no', as if they are recalling something that has happened during the day. If this happens, you can try to wake your child gently to reassure her as much as possible. If she can remember the dream, you may have to give her a lot of comfort before she will return to sleep. Be careful not to suggest ideas or scenes by saying something like 'Did you see a scary monster?' or 'Was it the bad man again?' – often parents do this trying to reassure their child but actually make things worse.

You need to reassure her that although her fears seem real, her dreams are not. You can help her to learn the difference and your confidence in her ability to cope with the nightmares will help her enormously. If you can't ban television altogether, try to keep tabs on what your child is watching, reading in books or seeing on her computer – avoid things that will compound her fears.

Night terrors

Despite being a very frightening experience to witness, a child who suffers from a night terror is not aware of it happening and will not remember it in the morning. Your child may give a piercing scream and be wide-eyed and anxious with dilated pupils, probably with sweat running down her forehead. If you go to pick her up or comfort her, you will notice her heart pounding and you may feel as though an evil spirit is trying to get out of your child. Your child will seem awake but is actually asleep. The night terror can last from a few seconds to over fifteen minutes. It is not advised to try to wake your child while the night terror is happening but you may like to sit and watch over her until it passes.

Night terrors are more common in boys than girls and occur in toddlers and preschoolers but can also affect older children. From my experience, they normally occur in the overtired child who is out of routine due to school holidays or friends or relatives visiting or some other disruption. If they are happening regularly, bringing your child's bedtime forward half an hour can often cause the night terrors to stop.

Night terrors always occur in the non-dreaming first third of your child's sleep, so before midnight, and normally at the exact same stage of sleep each night. I advise parents to stay with their child and note exactly what time they fall asleep, then look at the time the night terror starts. The next night, wake her up before the night terror is due to start. For example, if she went to bed at 7 pm but fell asleep at 7.21 pm and the night terror started at 10.14 pm, you would know the night terror started two hours and 53 minutes into sleep. The next night you would sit with your child until she falls asleep and then wake her two hours and 40 minutes later. If you do this for four nights running, the night terror pattern will usually be broken and they will disappear. When waking your child, do so slowly by talking to her, making sure she is fully awake. Your child will not be aware of the night terrors so will not be sure why you are waking her – you will have to come up with a good story, one that just can't wait until the morning. Night terrors don't harm or affect your child's sleep at all.

Sleepwalking

Sleepwalking occurs when the movement centre in the brain remains active during sleep. In children, sleepwalking is more common in boys than girls and often runs in families. Children who sleepwalk are usually between the ages of six and sixteen, and the episodes normally happen in the first third of sleep, before midnight. Sleepwalkers may wander around the house for up to 30 minutes and may get dressed, open the fridge or even the front door. With this in mind, it is very important to make the environment safe where the sleepwalking is taking place.

You should have the front door locked so that a child sleepwalking cannot open it but so you can in case of emergency.

Most sleepwalking children are unaware of what they are doing and won't remember anything about it in the morning, so it is usually more worrying for the parents when they discover their child trotting around. Avoid awakening her if she is sleepwalking, as this may frighten her. Simply steer her back to bed and ensure that she is safe. As overtiredness has been linked to sleepwalking, maintaining a bedtime routine will help minimise the problem. Putting your child to bed at the same time each night will avoid her getting overtired. Most sleepwalkers eventually stop on their own, although there are many adults who still wander around the house in pyjamas with a glazed expression!

Sleeptalking

Sleeptalking happens to children between three and ten years, again in the first third of the night (before midnight). It is impossible to hold a conversation with a sleeptalker – they tend to be talking to themselves and if you ask them a question you will only get a one-syllable answer. Children tend to be repeating the same thing while they talk in their sleep, saying things like 'it's mine' or 'get down', as if going over something that happened in their day. Like sleepwalking children, sleeptalkers do not remember the incident in the morning and tend to grow out of it.

Sleep discrepancies and sedatives

I do not believe that any child or baby should be given sedatives unless there is a very good medical reason for it. Giving sedatives to a baby or child because they have a sleep problem does not solve anything, it just puts the problem away to be solved at a later stage. And who knows – by then you could have an even bigger problem or even an addiction on your hands (the chances of a child or baby being addicted are slim, but a parent might become addicted to giving them to hide problems).

Children's sedatives can now only be obtained after receiving a prescription from a doctor, and if prescribed in the correct manner these drugs are quite safe. Beware, however, that children react in very different ways to sedatives. One child might fall straight into a deep sleep but another may just become drowsy or even hyperactive if too much or too little is given.

If your doctor has prescribed sedatives for a long-haul flight don't wait until you are 30,000 feet up in the air to test out the effects on your child – this would not be a good place for a hyperactive child or, even worse, an allergic reaction. Children normally drop off to sleep on flights anyhow due to the low oxygen levels.

FAMILY VARIATIONS

Not all families are in the typical 2.4-children average we often see and I have helped many parents adapt my routines to suit their circumstances and family's needs. The most common situations I come across are living in crowded accommodation and stepfamilies, so here are a few tips.

Living in crowded accommodation

For families living in one room, sleep problems are often very difficult to solve as babies can't help but see and hear what happens after bedtime so they often stay awake until their parents go to bed late in the evening. If this is your situation then you will have to adapt my routines to fit your circumstances.

If your accommodation is cramped, it's possible you use your baby's cot as a safe place for her to play during the day. But as a result, she may then find it hard to associate her cot with going to sleep, so you will need to have a very obvious sleep ritual for your baby as well as a comfort item that is only given at sleep times. Make the difference between sleep times and play time as clear as possible: use subdued lighting in the evening, have a regular bedtime routine at night and a good bedtime ritual before the day and night sleeps.

I suggest if you live in cramped accommodation you get a Japanese-style rice-paper screen or similar. You could then place this up just out of arms' reach of the cot, blocking your baby's view for all of her sleeps. This creates a clear distinction between waking and sleep time.

Your body language is very important during sleep times, so try not to look directly at her in the cot and avoid sudden movements in the room, keeping your voice low or even whispering until she's asleep.

Don't have the TV on while your baby is falling asleep as she may use it as an aid and then need it when drifting from one sleep cycle to the next during the night.

Being firm about bedtime routines is also very important. I know this can be difficult in cramped surroundings, and the temptation is there to let things slip because it's too hard. But if you persevere you'll be amazed at the results and will enjoy the fruits of your labour for years to come!

Stepfamilies and looking after other people's children

Stepfamilies are becoming more and more common. For this arrangement to work well, good communication between all involved parents is needed. This is not always possible but well worth trying in order to make everyone's lives easier.

It's certainly best that children coming into your home to stay the night follow your rules and boundaries, but this can become more difficult if the visiting children's natural parent feels guilty about the little time he or she gets to spend with them. Parents need to step outside their situation and realise that whatever decisions are made now will be the roots for how it develops in years to come. For example, if you now have an eighteen-month-old who follows your rules and boundaries but you allow your four- and six-year-old stepchildren, who visit every other weekend, flexibility in those rules, it will come to a point where your youngest child will notice the differences and start to resent the rules. At this point it may be too hard to try to change the more lax habits you have allowed to set in. Setting the rules from day one will both avoid this problem and help your stepchildren to bond with you faster because they will feel much more secure if they know where they stand. The most important thing, as in every family, is to maintain a united front. If one parent sets a different boundary or doesn't back the other up, you are asking for trouble. Agree on a plan, then stick to it.

When new families are formed, there are adjustments for both the children and the adults involved. There may be house moves, new step-parents and new children to get to know and build trust with, as well as new routines or new schools. It's important to maintain your children or stepchildren's habits and routines as much as possible, and that includes bedtime boundaries. If there are older children coming to stay, try to involve them in setting the new rules. Older stepchildren will adapt very quickly to one set of rules with you and another at home. If the stepchildren visiting are younger, it is worth talking to the other parents about what the rules and boundaries are at home. Lots of listening, talking and being honest and patient can help too.

COMMON QUESTIONS

If my baby's flat head syndrome needs to be corrected by a helmet, will they need to shave her head? No, shaving the head is not necessary. I have seen a few babies with these corrective helmets and they seem to upset parents more than babies.

Should I wake my seven-year-old up while he is having a night terror? No you should not try to wake up your son as this will only agitate him more and prolong the attack.

My doctor says my baby may have asthma. What can be done to prevent attacks? Some babies only have an asthma attack when they get a cold or other upper respiratory tract infection. These attacks are hard to prevent. Others have problems when they come into contact with an allergen, such as cat fur or dust mites, which triggers an attack. Keeping your child's room as dust-free as possible will help prevent the attacks. If you have a pet with fur you might be best to give it to a friend to look after and see if the attacks lessen.

12

COMMON HEALTH CONCERNS

Following are the most common problems parents contact me about in relation to their baby's health. If after reading this information you are still concerned about the health of your baby, please seek medical advice from your doctor or health visitor.

CHILDHOOD COMPLAINTS

Unfortunately, illness in childhood is unavoidable and will affect you and your baby at some time during the first couple of years. This is perfectly normal and during the toddler years children seem to come down with one childhood complaint after another. Babies are born with a well-developed immune system that can produce a variety of needed antibodies but this only lasts about a year. This is why vaccinations are usually given after the first year and why you will notice your child coming down more frequently with common childhood illnesses.

If your baby does become sick, it is very important to check on him frequently. Monitor his temperature and check the bedding is not wet from sweat if he is running a fever. You may also need to check your baby's bedding for vomit and nappy for diarrhoea, as well as regularly monitoring nappies for wetness as dehydration is a major concern with some illnesses. Please read the advice later in this chapter on dehydration.

When your baby is sick, try to stick to his routine as closely as possible. But if you notice that he is not taking as big a milk feed as usual, you may need to offer more frequent milk feeds or some water until he is well again. Don't worry about this affecting your routine – you will be able to get back on track when he is feeling better. You may also find that your baby needs to sleep more while he is unwell. It is all right not to wake him up for the scheduled feed times but don't let your unwell baby go longer than four hours in the day between feeds.

It is just as important for you to get some sleep while your baby is unwell as it is for him to, otherwise you won't have the energy to look after him. If you are finding it hard to sleep because you keep getting up to check on your baby, why not set up camp in his room? You might sleep better if you are closer to him. It is not advisable to take your baby into your own room or bed where he could get even hotter and overheat, plus it is easier for you to break the habit of sleeping in his room than to ask your baby to go back to sleeping in his own room.

The common cold

One of the hardest things for a new parent to do is watch their baby suffer through his first cold. He will be uncomfortable, snuffling and will probably have trouble feeding, but there are things you can do to make it easier on him. Babies get more colds because their immune systems are less developed than an adult's, and the average baby will have at least six colds in his first two years of life.

A cold is an upper respiratory infection caused by many different viruses. They are easily spread when someone who has a cold sneezes or coughs and the virus goes into the air and is inhaled by someone else. You can also catch a cold through hand-to-hand contact so you should always wash your hands after blowing your nose or cleaning your baby's nose.

A baby with a cold may have a fever of around 37.5°C, a cough, reddened eyes, a sore throat and a runny nose. Some babies become very irritable and lose their appetite. Young babies often find it hard to feed while they have a cold because they can't breathe through their blocked nose while they suck. It is a good idea to clean their nose before each feed. Some vapour rubs are available to help your baby breathe at night, but you are better to try them on his bedding than his skin as some babies hate the smell and get very upset.

If your baby has been sleeping through the night he will probably start waking while he has a cold. If this happens, go to him and comfort him but try not to feed him. If your baby has a fever you may have to give little feeds again in the night, but once the cold has gone use the appropriate settling guideline during the night.

A cold generally starts to go away after ten days but can sometimes last up to fourteen days. Breastfeeding is one of the best ways to protect your baby's health, since your baby will be getting your antibodies and natural immunities. Breastfed babies do still get colds but their symptoms are usually milder.

If you notice a friend or relative looking as if they have cold symptoms, ask them to wash their hands thoroughly before handling your baby or his things. If you or your partner smoke, try to give it up, and refrain from taking your baby to areas where someone has been smoking. Babies and children who live with cigarette smokers have more colds and their colds last longer than their unexposed peers.

If your baby is under three months old you should contact your doctor at the first sign of a cold or any illness, just to be on the safe side. If your baby is older than three months, contact your doctor if the cold isn't beginning to clear up after ten days or lasts longer than fourteen days, or if his temperature climbs above 39°C. You should also contact your doctor if your baby has an earache, breathing problems, wheezing, a persistent cough or constant thick, green mucus running from his nose.

With a cold, there is little you can do apart from ride it out and make your baby as comfortable as possible. Don't give him cold remedies without talking to a health professional first. If your baby is congested, elevate the head of the mattress as sleeping at an incline may help relieve his nasal drip. Do not use pillows to prop your baby up as they add to the risk of cot death. Wipe his nose regularly to help him breathe more easily, and you can apply petroleum jelly to the outside of his nostrils to reduce irritation. Never stick cotton buds up your baby's nose in an attempt to clear it – this will not help in any way. If your child is having trouble breastfeeding with a stuffy nose, you may like to ask your GP to prescribe saline drops to apply to each nostril fifteen minutes before a feed. Try a cool-mist vaporiser to moisten the air.

Ear infections

Babies often get ear infections after they have had a cold or a cough. This is because there is only a small tube extending between the ear and throat and infection can pass through it quite quickly. By the time they have started school, most children have had an ear infection of some form. I have also known some babies to get an ear infection every time they cut a tooth. I am sure the ear infection is not related to teething, but perhaps the baby's immune system is not working as well at that time. If you are at all concerned that your baby may have an ear infection, take him to see your doctor.

Ear infections are caused by bacteria or a virus in the external, middle or inner part of the ear. The most common type of ear infection in young children is called otitis media: *otitis* is the word given for inflammation of the ear and *media* refers to the part of the ear that is infected, in this case, the middle part. Ear infections are usually treated with antibiotics along with pain relief such as paracetamol, which will also help reduce any accompanying fever. You can also hold a warm cloth under your baby's ear while you hold his head to the side to help relieve the pain.

If your baby has an ear infection he will be in some pain, which means he may cry a lot and pull at his ear. He may suddenly be waking frequently at night, or he may be off his food and also refusing milk feeds. He could also have a raised temperature and you may notice he is not hearing as clearly as usual.

Repeated ear infection may lead to a condition called glue ear where some sticky fluid gets trapped in the middle ear. This can have an effect on your baby's hearing. If you feel that his hearing has not come back to normal a few weeks after an ear infection, consult your doctor as this could be an indication of glue ear. In most cases a decongestant helps clear the fluid but sometimes a small operation may be required to remove the fluid and dry out the ear.

Tonsillitis

Tonsillitis is not a problem that occurs in babies under two. I believe this is because the tonsils in a baby are too small to be checked for infection.

Babies do get red, sore throats when they are suffering from a cold, but this is not tonsillitis. Some babies need their tonsils and adenoids removed but usually for a different reason, for example if enlarged tonsils and adenoids cause problems breathing at night (sleep apnoea).

Croup

Croup, a common childhood virus which affects the larynx and trachea, is well-known for its sudden onset of a bark-like cough in young children. In adults we would call it laryngitis, but in babies and children the inflammation can swell the windpipe, making it difficult to breathe. Croup is more common in children between six months and three years old, although it can affect older children, and most often occurs in autumn and winter. Typically it's due to a mild upper respiratory tract infection caused by a variety of viruses.

If your baby has croup, you'll know. Your baby will either wake at night or during the day with a sudden coughing that sounds like a dog barking. Croup normally makes its first appearance in the middle of the night (you may have noticed that your baby had symptoms that you thought were due to a cold when you put him to bed). You need to go to him straight away as he will probably be very frightened at the sound coming out of him. It's best to treat croup immediately, especially if your baby is crying, which only exacerbates the symptoms.

If this is the first time your baby or toddler has had croup, you may want to call your doctor right away, even if it's the middle of the night. The GP on call may ask questions to try to determine the level of seriousness of the croup. He or she might then give you instructions either to try home remedies or to take your baby to the accident and emergency department of your local hospital for treatment. It is best to ask the doctor where the nearest children's hospital is – if there is one, with an A & E, in your area, it is often worth travelling the extra few minutes. If your child has had croup before, you might still want to call your doctor to be on the safe side, especially if your baby has a temperature of 39°C or above. Sometimes it is too hard for parents to wait for their doctor to come or even return their phone call and they feel safer just getting in the car and going to the nearest emergency department. In many cases, however, the child will improve significantly on his way to hospital. If your baby does not improve at the hospital, he may be given oral or inhaled steroids.

If your baby has noisy breathing and difficulty inhaling or is drooling, this can be a sign of a more serious bacterial infection, epiglottitis. The Hib vaccine that babies receive at two, four and twelve months has made epiglottitis all but non-existent, but it is still better to be safe when it comes to a young child, so contact your doctor or visit your nearest accident and emergency department immediately if you suspect this.

Croup is caused by a virus, so antibiotics won't help. To treat croup at home you need to be calming and reassuring to your toddler. If he is crying, try and stop him as the crying may make things worse. If he is breathing noisily or his breathing appears difficult you should sit him upright on your lap to help him breathe. If he has a fever follow my guidelines to help reduce it and also give him lots of cool drinks. Taking a child outside and walking around in fresh air, making sure you are carrying him upright, may also help.

In the past, people commonly advised taking a toddler into a steam-filled bathroom to loosen the mucus and make breathing easier, but there has been no evidence found to show that this does work and some children have been scalded by the steam so it is no longer recommended.

Putting a humidifier in your baby's room is also believed to help a baby with croup. And it is very important to encourage him to take extra fluids: give extra milk feeds to a young baby or extra water to an older baby or toddler. Warm soup may taste especially good if your toddler has lost his appetite for food.

Croup usually lasts for four to six days, peaking on the second or third night.

Fevers
A fever is when your baby's temperature becomes higher than normal due to an infection that his body is trying to fight. The infection is

normally caused by a virus or bacteria and is not always an indication of serious illness. Neither is the level of temperature always a good indicator of how sick your baby really is. You are much wiser to judge how sick he is by the way he is behaving. For example, I have seen a baby with chickenpox run a very high temperature while another with meningitis had a temperature indicating a fever but not high enough to cause too much concern. It was only when the baby with meningitis refused fluids and became floppy and sleepy that we got concerned and took him to hospital, where we discovered how sick he really was.

Your child's normal temperature should be between 36.5°C and 37°C; if it is higher than 37°C then he has a fever. To take your baby's temperature you can use a thermometer. Mercury or digital thermometers can be used under your baby's arm: hold him on your lap, placing the thermometer well up under the fold of his armpit and hold the arm flat against the side of his body for three minutes (or until the digital version signals to stop). **You should never put a thermometer in your baby's mouth or bottom.**

There is also the very easy-to-use thermometer strip which can be placed on your baby's forehead. I find them good as a guide but not very accurate.

A new type of thermometer which has come on the market over the last few years is the infra-red instant thermometer. I find this the easiest and fastest to use, but you need to keep a spare battery in the house. This is also the method most doctors are now using. Place the thermometer tip gently in baby's ear, as instructed, and press a button for an instant result. It is recommended you change the plastic cap after each use to ensure an accurate reading and for hygiene.

If your baby is under three months and has a fever of 37.5°C or over you should take him to see a doctor, unless your baby has recently had his immunisation (see advice on reactions to immunisations on pages 256–257). Babies of three to six months with a fever of 39°C or over should also be taken to the doctor unless related to immunisation. If your baby is over three months and has a temperature between 37.5°C and 39°C, this is regarded as a mild fever and can be treated at home unless he has other concerning symptoms.

To treat your baby's fever, undress and cool him down by sponging him with lukewarm water. **Never put a baby in a cold bath as shivering triggers the body to raise its temperature. Don't put a fan directly on a baby with a fever.** Dress your baby in light clothing such as a singlet and nappy, then check his temperature again. If it is still elevated, give some paracetamol according to the instructions on the bottle. Offer small amounts of water and extra breastmilk or formula feeds. Make sure your baby drinks at least the same amount as usual, but don't worry if he is off his food. Give him extra cuddles and attention while he is unwell.

Febrile convulsions (fever fits)

Febrile convulsions occur in 3 or 4 per cent of young children and babies, normally between one and six years and very rarely before nine months. They are caused by a rapid increase of the child's body temperature and usually occur when the temperature has jumped to over 39°C. They normally happen when your baby is getting a viral infection such as a respiratory infection, while the temperature is rising rapidly.

As frightening as it may look, it's important not to panic if a baby or young child has a febrile convulsion. During a convulsion your baby may go unconscious, stop breathing normally and be unaware of his surroundings. You will also see your baby go stiff or floppy, have jerky movements and his eyes may roll back in his head. The fits usually last between one to three minutes but on a very rare occasion may last up to fifteen minutes. If your baby is having his first fit and it goes for longer than five minutes, or if it stops and starts again, seek medical attention by calling an ambulance. If he has difficulties breathing after the fit, call an ambulance.

During a fit, do not try to restrain your baby or put anything in his mouth. Stay with, placing him on his side or tummy with his head to the side. Loosen any clothes around the neck area. Once the convulsion is over, take your baby to your doctor or a children's hospital to be checked over. The high temperature is usually related to a viral infection, but the doctor will want to be sure of the cause of the sudden high temperature and fit. Sometimes further investigations or blood tests are done to help find the cause.

When your baby or child has had one febrile convulsion, the chance of him having another in the next year is 30 per cent, and this will keep reducing as he gets older. By the time your child is six years old the chance of another is one in 10,000. Febrile convulsions are usually harmless and do not cause brain damage, epilepsy or any long-term condition. It is important to remember if your child has had a febrile convulsion to take extra-special care when controlling their next fever.

Diarrhoea and vomiting

Diarrhoea and vomiting occur in both breastfed and bottle-fed babies, although it is less common in breastfed babies. The most common cause of diarrhoea and vomiting in babies and toddlers is a viral infection such as gastroenteritis but it can also be caused by other things. Most babies will have the occasional bout of vomiting or diarrhoea and this is nothing to worry about; however, if it continues there is the concern that your baby could become dehydrated quite quickly. The younger your baby, the more serious dehydration is (see advice on dehydration in the next section).

Your baby should be taken to the doctor if he is less than six months and not keeping any milk down. Also take a baby of any age to your doctor if showing any of the following: bile-stained (greenish) vomit or signs of blood in the vomit; blood or mucus in poo; sleepier than normal or hard to wake up; limp; sunken eyes; dry mouth or tongue, or if your baby goes six hours or more without a wet nappy.

If you are breastfeeding and your baby is less than six months, continue to breastfeed but give smaller, more frequent feeds. Breastmilk contains antibacterial and antiviral proteins, and a mother also produces antibodies against her child's particular bug which pass through her breastmilk. If your baby is over six months then also give him cool, boiled water as often as you can.

If your baby is less than six months and formula-fed then you are best to talk to your health professional about what to do. If your baby is over six months, stop giving formula for twelve to 24 hours. I usually give an oral rehydration solution (ORS) such as Dioralyte, but you will need to ask your pharmacist which one is suitable for your baby's age. These contain the right amounts of sugar, salt and water to allow your baby's inflamed intestines to start absorbing water again, but they must always be made up with the correct amount of cool, boiled water. When vomiting and diarrhoea settles, or after 24 hours, start with half-strength formula for twelve to 24 hours, then full-strength. If symptoms return, consult your doctor.

Older babies and toddlers should be given clear fluids only for 24 hours. On day two, reintroduce starch-based solids such as pasta, rice, potato and bread. Avoid fatty foods for several days, as they can aggravate the diarrhoea.

Dehydration

The main causes of dehydration in babies are very hot weather or high fever, diarrhoea or vomiting but it can also be brought on by other factors. There are a few signs to look for if you think your baby may be becoming dehydrated:

- If your baby goes for more than six hours without a wet nappy. Often nappies can look dry but are actually wet – if in doubt, weigh an unused one and compare with the one you have just taken off.

- If your baby's urine has a very strong smell.

- If your baby keeps looking for a feed and then falls asleep after only a few sucks at the breast or takes no more than 30 ml (1 oz) of milk from a bottle.

- If his fontanelle (the soft bit on the top of his skull where the bones have not yet fused) is sunken.

- If your baby is very sleepy and lethargic.

- If his lips appear chapped.

The first thing to do if your baby appears dehydrated is get more fluid into him. Offer more frequent milk feeds and recommence your routine when the dehydration has passed. Offer some cool, boiled water even if breastfeeding – you may only get 2 or 3 ml (0.07 or 0.1 oz) in at a time, but keep trying (but don't give more than 30 ml (1 oz) of water between feeds). You can put water in your baby's mouth with a syringe or on a teaspoon. If you are able to get more fluid in and wet nappies reappear, there is nothing else you need to do.

However, if you struggle to get more fluid in and the nappies remain dry, you will need to contact your doctor. If your baby becomes very weak and listless, take him to hospital immediately.

> **Tip:** I recommend a breast- or bottle-fed baby be offered cool, boiled water in hot weather between feeds to avoid becoming dehydrated.

Rashes

A young baby's skin is very delicate, so rashes are a common event for most babies. Some of these rashes are heat or sweat rashes, some are due to a mild skin irritation from fabrics or detergents and some are due to mild viral illnesses. I have seen all sorts of rashes where I have not been able to work out the causes, but if your baby only has a rash and no other symptoms of an illness then you have nothing to worry about. If you are in doubt, contact your doctor or clinic nurse.

There are a few rashes you need to look out for, such as chickenpox, measles and German measles (rubella); however, these are very uncommon in babies and have other symptoms such as a fever. The dreaded meningitis rash has a very fierce red or purple appearance and looks like dots or bruises. A useful test if you think a rash is meningitis is to press the bottom of a glass against the rash and look through the glass at the rash. If it stays the same colour and doesn't fade, then this is a more worrying rash and could be meningitis. You should take your child straight to hospital.

A rash in a well, alert baby who is feeding normally isn't likely to be due to anything serious. It is important to see a doctor if the baby is also unwell, has a temperature, is not feeding properly, or is unusually irritable or drowsy. It is also wise to see a doctor if the rash lasts for more than a couple of days.

Cradle cap

Cradle cap is a skin condition commonly found on the scalp of babies. It usually appears in the first few weeks of life characterised by greasy, yellow, scaly patches on the skin of the baby's scalp. It is a form of dermatitis that is thought to be a result of hormonal changes which stimulate secretions from the oil glands in the skin. Cradle cap does not appear to be itchy or cause any distress to your baby nor is it contagious.

Mild cradle cap often goes away without treatment, but there are steps you can take which might help to soften it and remove it gently. Rub a little olive oil into your baby's scalp before bed and then wash your baby's hair in the morning with a mild shampoo. While washing his head, if you gently massage the scalp with a soft baby toothbrush you should be able to remove some of the flaky bits. Usually there is no other treatment required and the cradle cap stops developing as your baby gets older. On a rare occasion the doctor may choose to treat the cradle cap with a weak hydrocortisone cream, possibly along with a mild special baby shampoo. Very severe cases may be referred to a skin specialist. If you notice your baby's cradle cap spreading to his face or body consult your doctor.

On very rare occasions the cradle cap can get infected. If this happens you will see the skin become red and develop small blisters which may start to weep. This is caused by a germ called impetigo and if you notice this you should take your baby to the doctor. Very severe cases may be referred to a skin specialist. If you notice your baby developing eczema on his face or body consult your doctor.

TAKING YOUR BABY OR TODDLER TO THE DOCTOR

Finding a good doctor with whom you feel comfortable is a priority when you have young children. The doctor that you went to for years before having a baby may have been fantastic for you but might not be as good with you as a parent or your baby.

Before taking your baby to the doctor, prepare yourself for what might happen. Looking after a sick baby or toddler at home is one thing, but in a busy waiting room with lots of other people it might pay to imagine the worst-case scenario. For example, I was once at the doctor's with a very queasy three-year-old who pulled my top forward and vomited down my front – I had brought clean clothes for him but not for me!

The hardest part of taking an older baby or toddler to the doctor is keeping them occupied, so most doctors now have a play area in the waiting area and toys in consultation rooms. Don't worry if your baby who was really sick at home is now playing happily; the doctor will be used to seeing this. Quite often the change in scenery will make your baby feel better but if there is something wrong, the doctor will still find it. Let your toddler bring one or two of his favourite toys with him. This will not only keep him occupied but it will facilitate relationship development with the doctor and give your toddler confidence. Many toddlers will have played with a toy doctor's medical kit at home. These have huge value since they teach children about the instruments a doctor or nurse uses and therefore what to expect. Toddlers like to know what things are going to happen in advance as it helps them to feel safe and secure.

Try to remember to bring your baby record book along each time your baby needs to see the doctor or goes for immunisations or to hospital. Your doctor may not always want to see it but it's better to have it with you just in case. Write any questions down in case you become so busy juggling your child that you forget what you wanted to discuss until you get home and it is too late. Your doctor will not mind if you hand him or her the list while you look after your child.

Your doctor may ask:

- Is your baby feeding normally or wanting to feed more or less?

- Does your baby have a fever? If so, does paracetamol help to reduce it?

- Is your baby as alert or playing as usual?

- Has your baby wet his nappy within the last six to twelve hours?

- Has your baby had any vomiting or diarrhoea?

Then he or she may ask for more information about the illness and the specific symptoms. If, for example, the problem is vomiting, then it will help your doctor and save time if you have answers already prepared to questions such as the following:

- When did the vomiting start?

- How many times has he vomited in the past 24 hours?

- What colour is it and is there any blood in the vomit?

- Is it associated with diarrhoea or a fever?

Or if, for example, your baby has a rash, your doctor will ask things such as:

- How long has the rash been present?

- Where is the rash?

- Where did the rash start and where has it spread?

- Is your baby or toddler scratching the rash?

- Has the child been in contact with anyone with a similar rash?

Don't worry if you don't know all the answers – this will not make you look like a bad parent! Remember, you don't need to wait to be asked. Tell your doctor any detail that you think might be important, no matter how small or trivial it may initially seem.

Dressing your baby or toddler in suitable clothing that allows quick access to his tummy, chest and back will make things much easier all round. Most young babies can be moved around fairly easily for examinations, but many do not like having their ears examined. To do this properly and to avoid injury they need to be held firmly, and many babies don't like that either! There's a straightforward way of holding a baby for an ear examination – ask your doctor to show you and then practise it at home. This way you'll gain confidence and your baby will become used to it, making examination at the doctor's less stressful.

IMMUNISATION

Some potentially life-threatening childhood diseases are preventable through immunisation, an important consideration as babies' less-developed immune systems put them at bigger risk of infection than adults. Mothers pass some immunity to their babies but this eventually wears off. Childhood diseases are also a lot more serious in babies than in adults: for example, whooping cough is not usually very severe for an adult but for a baby it can be fatal. Another case in point is measles: one in every 25 babies with measles goes on to develop pneumonia, and about one in every 5,000 develops a brain inflammation which can lead to brain damage and even death. A good part to the immunisation story is that there is safety in numbers: if enough people are immunised, diseases like whooping cough and measles will start to disappear from a community altogether, like smallpox.

Recommended immunisations

Immunisation schedules and vaccines are constantly being revised. The following is a guide only – see your family doctor for more information.

Immunisations are considered very safe, however they may cause some minor side effects. Major side effects are extremely rare and health authorities agree the risk of the disease is far more serious than any side effects of the injection.

RECOMMENDED IMMUNISATION SCHEDULE (0 TO 4 YEARS)

Age	Dieseases immunised against	Vaccine given
2 months	Diphtheria, tetanus, pertussis (whooping cough), polio and Haemophilus influenzae type b Hib) Pneumococcal infection	DTaP/IPV/Hib and Pneumococcal conjugate vaccine (PCV)

255

Age	Dieseases immunised against	Vaccine given
3 months	Diphtheria, tetanus, pertussis, polio and Haemophilus influenzae type b (Hib) Meningitis C (meningococcal group C)	DTaP/IPV/Hib and MenC
4 months	Diphtheria, tetanus, pertussis, polio and Haemophilus influenzae type b (Hib) Meningitis C Pneumococcal infection	DTaP/IPV/Hib, MenC and PCV
Around 12 months	Haemophilus influenzae type b (Hib) and meningitis C	Hib/MenC
Around 13 months	Measles, mumps and rubella (German measles) Pneumococcal infection	MMR and PCV
3 years and 4 months or soon after	Diphtheria, tetanus, pertussis and polio Measles, mumps and rubella	DTaP/IPV or dTaP/IPV and MMR

Routine Childhood Immunisation Programme, *A Quick Guide to Childhood Immunisations*, Department of Health Leaflet © Crown 2006. Reproduced by permission.

Minor side effects

- Localised pain, redness and swelling at injection site. Sometimes a small, hard lump may appear – this is no cause for concern.

- Low-grade temperature (fever).

- Grizzly, unsettled behaviour may persist for 24 to 48 hours.

- Drowsiness.

- Occasionally your baby will get diarrhoea with the polio immunisation.

- Five to twelve days after the measles, mumps and rubella immunisation, the following side effects may happen: a faint, non-infectious rash; a head cold; runny nose; cough; or puffy eyes.

What to do

- Give extra fluids to drink and milk feeds.

- Do not overdress your baby if hot – keep him cool.

- Give paracetamol to lower fever if needed.

If adverse symptoms following immunisation are severe and persistent, or if you are worried about your baby, contact your doctor or hospital.

COMMON QUESTIONS

How will I know if my baby is ill? The best way of telling if your baby is ill or in pain is not by his crying but by his behaviour. An ill or seriously distressed baby will look, behave and sound different. Signs to watch for include: looking pale, floppy or less active than normal; holding or rubbing his ear or tummy; or breathing differently, more rapidly or irregularly than normal. His cry may be much higher pitched than normal or he may be whimpering or moaning. If your baby feels hot to touch, check if it is a fever with a thermometer as crying may increase skin temperature but will not increase his body temperature. Conversely, your baby may feel cold and clammy when ill.

What if my baby's temperature is below 36.5°C? If your baby's temperature is below normal but he is acting normal then your thermometer is most likely not accurate. Try taking your own temperature. If your baby is cold to touch or floppy, get medical help immediately.

Why do children enrolling in school need to show an immunisation record? This proves they have been immunised against childhood diseases. Where there are gaps, health visitors encourage parents to ensure their children are given all the appropriate immunisations.

What causes otitis media? When a child has a cold, throat infection or a nasal allergy like hay fever, the Eustachian tube between ear and throat can become blocked, causing a build-up of fluid in the middle ear. If bacteria or a virus infects this fluid, it can cause swelling of the eardrum and pain in the ear, otherwise known as otitis media.

13

COT DEATH

WHAT IS COT DEATH?

Cot death, also known as Sudden Infant Death Syndrome (SIDS), refers to the sudden unexpected death of a baby from no known cause. I have decided to dedicate a whole chapter to cot death to help prevent other families experiencing the grief my family did, when I lost my brother to it. The number of babies dying of cot death is dropping and this is probably due to the Back to Sleep campaign in 1991 which educated parents and carers to always place a baby on her back to sleep with her face and head uncovered and keep her in a smoke free environment. The statistics given by FSID (the Foundation for the Study of Infant Deaths) shows that 300 babies still die each year from cot death in the UK. I believe this number could be reduced even further if all parents followed the guidelines given in the Back to Sleep campaign as some parents are becoming complacent and worrying about babies vomiting while on their backs or suffering from 'flat head syndrome'. As discussed earlier, a healthy baby sleeping on her back is actually at a much lower risk of choking on vomit than a baby sleeping on her tummy. Additionally, less than 2 or 3 per cent of babies develop 'flat head syndrome'. I worry cot death could start to rise again because I see parents using too little bedding due to concerns about overheating their babies and they are letting them go to sleep cold. Babies that are cold during sleep time learn to turn to their sides or tummies to warm up. If your baby is dressed correctly in a safe baby sleeping bag and covered with enough blankets she will sleep well on her back. The risk of overheating is very minimal: cot death research shows that the important point in preventing overheating is to ensure that your baby's head and face are not covered during sleep. For help in dressing your baby and covering her with the correct amount of bedding please see the safe bedding guide available at the Save Our Sleep website.

Cot death is the most common cause of death in babies between one month and one year of age but the majority of babies who die of cot death are under six months of age. More babies die of cot death in winter than summer. To this day, the cause of cot death remains unknown and there is no way of predicting which babies it will affect.

Babies and young children spend a lot of their time sleeping, so you need to be aware that some sleeping arrangements are not safe and can increase the risk of cot death or cause fatal sleeping accidents. Research has found some important ways to reduce the risk of cot death and create a safe sleeping environment for babies and young children. This chapter provides you with information to help you create such an environment for your baby or child.

CIGARETTE SMOKE IS LINKED TO COT DEATH

Cigarette smoke harms babies before and after they are born. Parents who smoke during pregnancy and after the birth of their baby increase the risk of cot death for their baby. In fact, if a mother smokes then the risk doubles, and if father smokes too it doubles again. There is still an increased risk of cot death if parents smoke outside, away from the baby, and if smoking parents co-sleep with their babies the risk of cot death is increased again. The reasons for this are not clear. However, we do know that being a non-smoker or smoking less will reduce the risk for your baby. Try not to let anyone smoke near your baby and try not to let anyone smoke in your house, your car or anywhere else your baby spends time.

If you want to quit smoking and you're not finding it easy, ask for help. Call the NHS Smokefree helpline on 0800 0224332 or ask your doctor, midwife or health visitor for information and advice.

SAFE SLEEPING

Sleeping a baby on her back reduces the risk of cot death. The chance of babies dying of cot death is greater if they sleep on their tummies or sides. Healthy babies placed to sleep on their backs are also less likely to choke on their vomit than babies placed on their tummies to sleep.

Babysitters, nannies, staff at day care centres and other people who care for your baby may not know that tummy- and side-sleeping increase the risk of cot death. Explain this to them before you leave your baby in their care.

Older babies who can turn over and move around the cot should be put to bed on their backs but then let them find their own sleeping position. The risk of cot death in babies over six months is extremely low.

Make sure your baby's face and head stay uncovered while she is sleeping. A good way to ensure this is to put her feet at the bottom of the cot so that she can't slip down underneath the bedclothes. Tuck in bedclothes securely so they can't become loose. Never put quilts, duvets, pillows, sheepskins or cot bumpers in a cot or under the sheet covering the mattress. All these are thought to increase the risk of cot death. You might decide to use a safe sleeping bag to help keep your baby's bedding in place but these should be used with bedding and not as an alternative to bedding. If you do use one, make sure it has a fitted neck and arm-holes like the one I recommend.

Taking a baby into an adult bed may be unsafe as the baby could get caught under the adult bedding or pillows. The baby could also get trapped between the bed and the wall, or fall out of the bed, or an adult could roll onto the baby if they are sleeping very deeply or have taken any drugs or alcohol.

Tips:

- Make sure your baby's head remains uncovered during sleep.

- Do not put your baby to sleep on a waterbed or beanbag.

- Tummy play is safe and good for babies when they are awake and an adult is present, but never put your baby on her tummy to sleep.

- Put your baby on her back to sleep.

- Tuck in your baby's bedclothes securely.

- Use a firm, clean and well-fitting mattress. Press your hand down firmly on the surface of the mattress. If you can still see the imprint of your hand, the surface is too soft for a baby to sleep on.

- Purchase a cot with four slatted sides without an enclosed end – the more air circulation, the lower the risk of cot death.

- Never use a plastic or PVC mattress protector in the cot because this stops air circulation and causes a baby to sweat.

- Never use a baby sleeping bag made from a stretch material such as jersey.

- Never use a baby sleeping bag with a zip down the side.

- Never use a baby sleeping bag with poppers or buttons on the shoulders.

- Never tuck your baby's sleeping bag in under the cot mattress.

- Before using a baby sleeping bag make sure it has fitted neck and arm holes and check that your baby's head cannot slip into the bag.

Safe places to sleep

Cots

All new and secondhand cots should carry the BSI number BS EN 716:1996. If you cannot find this, do not risk buying the cot.

If you are using an old or secondhand cot in particular, check for the following problems:

- Wobbly or broken parts that make the cot less stable.

- Bars a toddler or baby could get caught between (shouldn't be less than 50 mm or more than 85 mm).

- Knobs, corner posts or exposed bolts that could hook onto a toddler's or baby's clothing, especially around the neck.

- Too much space (more than 25 mm) between mattress and cot edge.

- Sides that are too low and can be climbed over by active little toddlers.

- Sharp catches or holes in the wood that can hurt curious fingers.

- Old paint that might contain poisonous lead.

- Solid ends reduce the air circulation in a cot. I recommend open-slatted cots on all four sides.

Babies can become trapped in a tilted rocking cot or cradle. If you have a rocking cradle or cot with a locking pin, make sure you secure the pin firmly in place whenever you leave your baby and check to make sure the cradle cannot move in your absence.

Portable travel cots

Always use the firm mattress that is supplied with the cot and don't place additional padding under or over the mattress as your baby may become trapped face-down in the gaps created between the mattress and the cot wall.

I do not recommend any portable cot that comes with an inflatable mattress. If the valve leaks then air can escape, leaving a sleeping surface that could be too soft and increase the risk of a sleeping accident.

Tip: For more information on cot death please visit the FSID website www.fsid.org.uk.

Sleeping dangers

The following are dangerous things to look out for and avoid wherever your toddler or baby sleeps – both during the night and for any daytime sleep or naps. Check both your own home and anywhere else your child is cared for, including day care, childcare centres and the homes of family and friends.

Safe bedding

An unsupervised adult bed may be unsafe for babies or toddlers because they could get caught under bedding or pillows, become trapped between the wall and the bed or fall out. The risk of accident is increased if you leave the baby or toddler alone on an adult bed or bunk bed.

Never put your baby or toddler in a soft place to sleep because her face may become covered. If you fall asleep with your baby while on a couch or sofa, there is a very high risk of a sleeping accident. Babies don't need pillows or cushions as they are too soft and can cover baby's face. Don't ever put your baby or toddler on a waterbed or beanbag.

Dangling cords or string

Keeps your baby's cot away from any cords hanging from blinds, curtains or electrical appliances because they could get caught around your baby's neck. You will also need to keep hanging mobiles out of the reach of her curious little hands and mouth.

Heaters and electrical appliances

Keep heaters or any electrical appliances well away from the cot to avoid the risk of overheating, burns and electrocution. Don't use electric blankets, hot-water bottles or wheat bags for babies or young children. Remember that your toddler or baby cannot escape from a bed or cot to cool down and does not know how to remove bedclothes. A baby that becomes too hot is at an increased risk of cot death.

COMMON QUESTIONS

Is it safe to put my newborn baby on his back to sleep? What happens if he vomits? Yes, healthy newborn babies can be safely placed on the back to sleep. Healthy babies sleeping on their back are less likely to choke on vomit than tummy-sleeping infants. Some babies with rare medical conditions might have to sleep on the side or the tummy.

Can babies be put on the tummy to play? Yes, tummy play is safe and very good for babies when they are awake and an adult is present. Tummy play helps muscle development in the arms, neck and back and prepares babies for crawling.

Is side-sleeping safe? Side-sleeping can increase the risk of cot death, possibly because a young baby can roll onto her tummy from her side. A baby sleeping on her back cannot roll onto her tummy until about five or six months of age, when most of the risk for cot death has passed.

Will formula-feeding increase the risk of cot death? There is no consistent evidence that bottle-feeding increases the risk of cot death or that breastfeeding reduces the risk.

If I sleep my baby in the same room as me will it reduce the risk of cot death? Research indicates that sleeping a baby in the same room, but not in the same bed, as the parents in the first six to twelve months of life may be protective. This is thought to be because parents can easily see the baby and check she is safe. This protective effect does not transfer if a baby sleeps in a room with other children, probably because children do not know if an infant is safe or not.

Is it okay to fall asleep on the couch with my baby? Some research into cot death has shown that an adult sleeping on a couch with a baby can be dangerous because the baby may accidentally become wedged between cushions or the back of the sofa. Put your baby into her own bed before you doze off if you feel yourself getting sleepy.

Will bed-sharing increase the risk of cot death? Bed-sharing does not appear to increase the risk of cot death for any of the following groups:

- When you bed-share to feed and cuddle your baby then put her back in her cot.

- When the baby is older than four months.

- If you and your partner are non-smokers.

If you or your partner smokes, sleeping with your baby, in the first four months may increase the risk of cot death. Particular circumstances that may increase the risk for all parents include when you or your partner have consumed alcohol or have taken drugs, which make you sleep more heavily.

If you sleep with your baby, make sure the bedding cannot cover her head and keep her away from the pillows. Use lightweight blankets rather than quilts or duvets and place your baby in a position where there is no risk of her falling out of the bed or becoming wedged in.

I am not sure what to dress my baby in at bedtime. What do you suggest? A useful guide is to dress baby as you would dress yourself – to be comfortably warm, not hot. Conversely, some parents underdress their baby, worrying she will get too hot. Babies mainly keep themselves cool through their head, in particular their face, so make sure baby's face and head remain uncovered and she will stay comfortably warm. Remove hats or bonnets from a baby as soon as you come indoors or enter a warm car, bus or train, even if it means waking your baby up. Babies regulate their temperature through their head.

For an up-to-date guide on how to dress your baby for sleeps at different nursery temperatures and in different climates please see the safe bedding guide available at the Save Our Sleep website.

We live in a very cold part of the country. How should we sleep our baby? Current research suggests that if your baby becomes either too hot or too cold, the risk of cot death is increased. To prevent this you need to use your own judgement, depending on where you live, and whether it is summer or winter. Dress your baby to be comfortably warm as you would dress yourself, not hot or cold. Another option is to use a heating system with a thermostat so you can set the room at one temperature.

Does dummy use reduce the risk of cot death? Some research indicates an apparent decrease in the incidence of cot death with dummy use, but the evidence is not overwhelming and the other effects of using a dummy outweigh this fact. One major reason not to use one is that babies who suck on dummies tend to have an increased risk of ear infections, which in turn may bring on high fevers and the use of antibiotics (both of which have side effects of their own).

What do we do now that our baby has started to roll over onto her tummy? Most cot deaths occur when babies are under six months of age and generally babies who are placed on their back to sleep cannot roll onto their tummies until about five or six months of age, when most of the risk has passed. Try not to let your baby sleep on her tummy before six months of age. You could put her in a safe infant sleeping bag as these delay babies rolling over.

Older babies who can turn over and move around the cot should be put on their backs to sleep and allowed to find their own sleeping position. The risk of cot death in babies over six months is extremely low.

Remember to reduce the risk in other ways: make sure that baby is on a firm, well-fitting mattress and don't tuck the bed covers in firmly if baby is on her tummy. Make sure her face and head remain uncovered during sleep and keep her smoke-free. Make sure she has supervised tummy time when awake to strengthen her upper body muscles.

My grandmother says I should put a hat on my five-week-old baby to make him sleep better. What do you think? I have heard this a few times and believe it to be a very dangerous old wives' tale. You should most definitely not put a hat on your baby to help him sleep as this could cause your baby to overheat and will increase the risk of cot death. If your baby is too hot and needs to cool down, he will need to be able to lose that heat through his head. You may put a hat on him if you are outdoors in cold weather, but take it off once inside.

FROM THE PARENTS

I was at a point where I had told my husband that we were not having any more kids because Kayla was a terrible sleeper and the sleep deprivation was driving me mad. Since being on your routine for about ten days, Kayla has two good, two-hour sleeps during the day and a 45-minute nap in the afternoon, she no longer has a dummy and she self-settles! I will definitely be putting our next bub on your routines from the start (yes, there is light at the end of the tunnel now and I can actually imagine giving Kayla a brother or sister!)

Joanne, Sydney

Phoenix started on your routines at about seven months of age. She had started napping during the day and was having difficulties going down for sleeps. Phoenix had to learn to self-settle and resettle herself without the use of a dummy or being fed. Within a few days, my husband and I saw dramatic results, Phoenix started sleeping through the night and during the day. Thank you, you have turned me into a confident mother who is looking forward to having other children and new challenges.

Veronica, Australia

My son is nearly twelve weeks old and has been on your routines since he was four weeks old. Before then he cried a lot. I loved your book but had questions that I didn't have answers to, and then I found your website.

We still have a few issues to iron out but the information I have received from everyone in the online advice area has been amazing, and every day I see improvements. Since starting the routines I have a happy smiling baby and I enjoy him so much more now that he is content.
Holly, Melbourne

Two years ago I was really struggling. Not once through my pregnancy did anyone allude to how difficult it was to get a child to sleep – let alone have them stay asleep – so it came as such a shock when my daughter started catnapping and waking every twenty minutes, day and night. I was rocking her to sleep for every sleep and some nights it was taking me and my husband five hours to get her to go to down for those twenty minutes. Luckily, someone recommended you and I ended up getting your one-on-one help. When my now fourteen-week-old son, Julian, came along I was adamant I was not going to make the same mistakes. I put him onto your routines from day one and I now have this remarkable little boy who loves to giggle and play and is already sleeping through the night for me. What more could I ask for?
Helen, **Steven**, **Emily** and **Julian**, Australia

Just wanted to write you a quick note to thank you for your book! It has worked wonders with my daughter Sarah, who we were rocking to sleep and feeding through the night for about three months. I always had something to blame it on, teeth, cold, etc... But now I know it was mainly due to her sleep cycles and the fact she could not put herself back to sleep. After five days using the lay-down technique she is off to sleep in no time. Last night she had a little cry for about one minute then off to sleep. I cannot begin to thank you enough ... My husband and I are starting to feel human again.
Katherine, Australia

I just wanted to say thank you. A friend gave me your article on catnapping and I put my baby on your routine the next day. Three weeks later she's still sleeping all night with two two-hour naps each day. Her father and I are still in shock that your routine has changed our lives forever.
Kim, Sydney

After one night of the 'deep-end approach', our baby son Connor (fourteen months) slept the longest in his life, nine hours straight. We had tried controlled crying for four weeks before giving up, but with your approach there were no tears and quick results. On day three he slept twelve hours straight with no protest – wow! I can't thank you enough.
Sara, Los Angeles, USA

My mummy and daddy were told by three doctors that I had colic and would grow out of it – till my mummy read your article on 'colic' and it disappeared the very next day. Thank you, Tizzie, for helping them fix me. I hope I can meet you one day.
From Samantha (now three months), Perth

I was dreading starting the new routine. However, I was very surprised on the first evening when having fed Jack then bathed him, I put him in his cot awake, switched off the light and, after about ten minutes of rolling around and babbling on to himself, he fell asleep. When he did start to cry I just placed my hand on his back to let him know I was there, then when he stopped I moved it away – he slept all night from 7 pm till 6.40 am. His wake times vary from 6 till 6.40 each morning.
Kay, London, UK

I just wanted to say thank you so much ... Your book is such an answer to a prayer! No one tells you how important it is to teach your baby to self-settle ... I now have a baby who puts himself to sleep, with no fuss at all, settles himself back to sleep if he wakes up, sleeps longer than 40 minutes during the day and now sleeps through the night. This is how it should be. I can now enjoy my beautiful, long-awaited baby. Thank you so much.
Sarah, UK

APPENDIX

First foods – alphabetical

Apples: From 4 months – peeled, cored, cooked and given as a purée.

Apricots: From 6 months – stoned, cooked and given as a purée, or raw from 8 months.

Asparagus: From 7 months as a finger food.

Aubergine: From 9 months in a meal.

Avocado: From 6 months – mashed.

Bananas: From 6 months – raw as a purée (look out for constipation).

Bean sprouts: From 12 months as a finger food.

Beans (green): From 5 months – cooked and given as a purée.

Beans (pulses): From 8 months – may cause wind and some babies find them hard to digest.

Beef: From 9 months in casseroles.

Beetroot: From 9 months in a meal.

Berries: From 12 months – be careful with strawberries as some babies may have an allergic reaction.

Bread: From 10 months – try a small amount of wheat in breakfast cereal first. The reason I say not to give bread is because your baby can make it into a ball in his mouth and choke on it.

Broccoli: From 6 months – cooked and given as a purée.

Brussels sprouts: From 8 months – be careful as can cause an upset tummy.

Butter: From 6 months in a small amount while cooking.

Butternut squash: From 4 months – peeled, cooked and given as purée.

Cabbage: From 8 months.

Carrots: From 4 months – cooked and given as a purée.

Cauliflower: From 6 months – cooked and given as a purée.

Celery: From 18 months as a finger food.

Cheese: From 6 months – give in very small amounts initially and watch for a reaction.

Chicken: From 6 months – puréed in a casserole.

Corn on the cob: Not recommended until your child has a full set of teeth, so around 2½ years.

Courgette: From 4 months – cooked and given as a purée.

Couscous: From 7 months.

Cucumber: From 10 months as a finger food.

Custard: From 2½ years – contains eggs so watch for a reaction.

Dried fruit (currants, raisins, sultanas): From 8 months.

Egg whites: From 12 months – look out for a reaction.

Egg yolk: Hard-boiled yolk can be given from 9 months – look out for a reaction.

Figs: From 9 months.

Fish: From 6 months – look out for a reaction.

Fruits: From 12 months (unless individually listed otherwise).

Garlic: From 9 months in very small amounts.

Grapefruit: From 5 years – may cause an allergic reaction.

Grapes: From 5 years.

Honey: From 12 months (but see note on page 121).

Kiwifruit: From 5 years – may cause an allergic reaction.

Lamb: From 6 months in a casserole.

Leek: From 8 months.

Lentils: From 6 months.

Lettuce: From 12 months – can be given raw.

Liver: From 9 months in small amounts (to my amazement, lots of babies like it!)

Mango: From 6 months – raw, mashed or puréed.

Melon: From 8 months as a finger food.

Milk: From 12 months in small amounts added to foods – watch for a reaction. As a drink from 14 months.

Mushrooms: From 9 months in casseroles.

Nuts: I would *never* give whole nuts to a child less than 5 years old – see note on page 121. This includes spreads such as nutella and peanut butter.

Oats: From 6 months in a breakfast cereal.

Onion: From 8 months – remove skins, dice and cook in casseroles.

Parsnips: From 8 months – cooked and mashed.

Pasta: From when your baby is eating finger foods, but not before 8 months.

Peaches: From 6 months – cooked and given as a purée.

Pears: From 4 months – cooked and given as a purée.

Peas: From 6 months – cooked and given as mash or purée.

Peppers: From 7 months in casseroles.

Pineapple: From 12 months as a finger food.

Plums: From 12 months in very small amounts – look out for a reaction.

Potatoes: From 4 months – cooked and given as a purée.

Prunes: From 9 months.

Pumpkin: From 8 months – cooked and given as mash or purée.

Rice: From 7 months – cooked.

Rice-based infant cereal: From 4 months.

Rhubarb: From 8 months – cooked and mashed.

Shellfish: From 18 months – look out for a reaction.

Spinach: From 7 months – cooked.

Swede: From 4 months – cooked and given as a purée.

Sweet corn: From 8 months (don't be surprised if you find it in your baby's nappy!)

Sweet potato: From 5 months – cooked and given as a purée.

Tomatoes: From 8 months – raw, skinned and seeded or cooked and given in meals.

Turnip: From 5 months – cooked and given as a purée.

Vegetable oil: From 8 months in cooking.

Wheat-based infant cereal: From 7 months – look out for a reaction.

Yoghurt: From 7 months – look out for a reaction.

INDEX

NOTES

NOTES

NOTES

NOTES

NOTES

NOTES

NOTES

NOTES